A FACE FROM THE WAR. *Pvt. Edwin Francis Jennison, of a Georgia regiment, killed at Malvern Hill. (See entry 17.)*

THE AMERICAN

Civil War

A CENTENNIAL EXHIBITION

U.S. LIBRARY OF CONGRESS

WASHINGTON, 1961

L.C. Card 61–60091

For sale by the Superintendent of Documents, U.S. Government Printing Office
Washington 25, D.C. - Price $1.50

Contents

Symbols of Custodial Divisions

G   General Collections
M   Map Division
MSS   Manuscript Division
MUS   Music Division
P   Prints and Photographs Division
R   Rare Book Division

Note for the Reader

In the descriptions of the items displayed, the titles of books, pamphlets, and periodicals have been given in italics.   The titles of broadsides (including music broadsides), engravings, lithographs, and drawings—all taken from the pieces exhibited—have been rendered in Roman within quotation marks.   Titles of sheet music, printed general orders, and all supplied titles (*e.g.,* of certain manuscript items), are in Roman (without quotes), as are also the titles of Forbes drawings whenever they are wanting on the originals and have been supplied either from copies of original mounts which accompanied the drawings or from the publication *Catalogue, Forbes Historical Art Collection of Battles, Incidents, Characters and Marches of the Union Army by Edwin Forbes* (n.p., 1881).   Bibliographic information such as the place and date of publication, when editorially supplied, is enclosed within square brackets.

Preface

IN THE YEARS 1961–65 the people of the United States will observe the centennial of the Civil War. This exhibit is presented as a part of the national commemoration.

The materials displayed have been taken exclusively from the collections of the Library of Congress. The arrangement is intended to illustrate, insofar as space and materials will permit, the tragic struggle of 1861–65 in as broad a scope as possible. This involves consideration of some of the political, economic, and social aspects of American life as they affected, and were affected by, the war. Military scenes and events predominate, but no attempt has been made to present a chronology of the war. Nor has it been possible to treat any of the complex issues in extended detail.

No single event in American history has received the attention which has been devoted to the Civil War, its causes and consequences. For this study, the resources of the Library of Congress are particularly rich and valuable. The Manuscript Division contains papers of many of the political and military leaders of the period, both Confederate and Union. Some, but by no means all, of these collections—the most notable being the Robert Todd Lincoln—are represented in this exhibit. The Map Division, in addition to other material relating to the war, contains the maps, diaries, correspondence, and private papers of Jedediah Hotchkiss, one of the most noted of Confederate cartographers. The Music Division has an assemblage of Civil War sheet music numbering in the thousands. The Rare Book Division houses numerous rare Confederate imprints; the distinguished collection of Lincolniana brought together by Alfred Whital Stern; and a large quantity of broadsides, including Union and Confederate recruiting posters, newspaper extras, and printed general orders. Finally there are the varied and comprehensive collections of the Prints and Photographs Division, from which are drawn the majority of the exhibit's pictorial materials. Included are photographic negatives made by Mathew B. Brady and the staff of field photographers organized by him to prepare a camera record of the war, original drawings by leading newspaper combat artists such as Edwin Forbes and Alfred R. Waud, and lithographic views of the war. Many of the drawings were shown early in 1961 at the National Gallery of Art as part of its display "The Civil War; a Centennial Exhibition of Eyewitness Drawings" and were subsequently circulated by the Smithsonian Institution Traveling Exhibition Service. The lithographic views—a still largely neglected field as far as students of the period are concerned—range from inaccurate portrayals of battle action by Currier and Ives to the carefully reproduced "on-the-spot" sketches of soldier-artists, foremost of whom, as far as the Library's holdings are concerned, was Pvt. Alfred E. Mathews (31st Ohio), over 35 of whose published drawings, among the finest of all Civil War lithographs, are in the collections.

This publication, which serves as a companion to the Library's *Abraham Lincoln: an Exhibition at the Library of Congress in Honor of the 150th Anniversary of his Birth* (1959), was prepared by Lloyd A. Dunlap, Consultant in Civil War Studies, and by Arthur G. Burton, Exhibits Specialist, under the general direction of Herbert J. Sanborn, Exhibits Officer of the Library of Congress.

Catalog

OF THE EXHIBIT

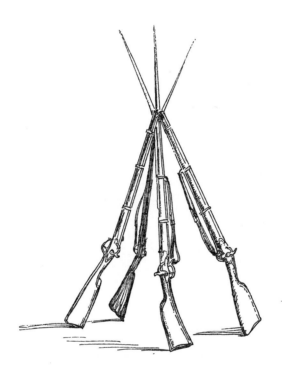

SEEDS OF CONFLICT

Years of sectional strife and mounting tensions preceded the great American tragedy of 1861–1865. Underlying the dispute was the obvious issue of slavery; but this problem, once thought to be in the process of peaceful and natural solution, involved numerous other complex factors, such as national politics, the conflict between agrarian and industrial economies, the rapid expansion of the Middle West, the interpretation of the Declaration of Independence and the Constitution, and wide differences in attitudes and cultures. Minorities, North and South, led by men of sincere but extreme points of view, were increased by such events as the civil war in Kansas, the Dred Scott decision, and John Brown's raid at Harper's Ferry. Moderation and compromise failed; emotionalism replaced reason; and the growing nation was plunged into its greatest internal crisis.

1. MRS. STOWE LIGHTS A TORCH IN THE NORTH

Harriet (Beecher) Stowe. *Uncle Tom's Cabin.* With 27 Illustrations on Wood by George Cruikshank, Esq. London, 1852. R

Millions who disliked the intolerance and fanaticism of the extreme abolitionists were moved by the words of Harriet Beecher Stowe, a housewife and the mother of seven children. A member of a family of famed theologians, all passionately devoted to the antislavery cause, Mrs. Stowe lived in Cincinnati, in close proximity to slavery, for 18 years, and returned to her native New England at a time when controversy over the Fugitive Slave Law of 1850 was at it height. Here she wrote *Uncle Tom's Cabin; or, Life Among the Lowly.* First published serially in *The National Era,* a Washington, D.C., antislavery paper, the work was issued in book form in 1852, selling 10,000 copies within a week, 300,000 copies within a year, and over a million copies by 1860. Denounced as inaccurate and unjust in the South, the book gave millions in the North and Europe their picture of slavery. Its widespread reception in England is attested to by the publication in 1852 of more than 20 London editions, one of which is exhibited.

2. SLAVERY DEFENDED "BY AN AMERICAN"

[David Christy] *Cotton is King; or, The Culture of Cotton, and its Relation to Agriculture, Manufactures and Commerce; to the Free Colored People; and to Those who Hold That Slavery is in Itself Sinful.* By an American. Cincinnati, 1855. G

The majority of Southerners owned no slaves at all; only a minute percentage owned them in large numbers; and in the area antislavery societies had once been more prevalent than in the North. The invention of the cotton gin had made the large-scale production of cotton possible and provided a more profitable use for slave labor; the economy of large areas became committed to a single crop and the labor force which produced it. Resenting indiscriminate and inflammatory attacks from areas where slavery was not needed or wanted, some spokesmen for the South defended slavery. Extremists, emphasizing the paternalistic aspects of the institution, proclaimed it as a positive good and advanced the theory that cotton and slavery, to which it was inextricably bound, were the controlling elements in the national economy. This "King Cotton" doctrine unrealistically ignored the agrarian South's dependence upon the manufacturing and financial interests of the North, where industry was rapidly replacing agriculture as the chief economic concern.

3. THE COLLAPSE OF THE DEMOCRATIC PARTY IN 1860

"Progressive Democracy—Prospect of a Smash Up." Lithographic cartoon by Currier & Ives, New York, 1860. (*See illustration.*) P

The nominating conventions of 1860 reflected the tragically divided state of public opinion. The Democratic convention met in Charleston, S.C., in April and adjourned without naming a candidate after heated debate over a platform which would guarantee slave property in the territories. In Baltimore, in June, separate conventions met and nominated Stephen A. Douglas of Illinois, representing the Northern wing of the party, and John C. Breckinridge of Kentucky, the candidate of the extreme Southern element. Also in Baltimore, fragments of the old Whig and American parties united under the name of the Constitutional Union Party, ignored the slavery issue, pleaded for the preservation of the Union, and nominated John Bell of Tennessee for the Presidency. Candidates for Vice President were Herschel V. Johnson, a Georgia unionist, Joseph Lane of Oregon, and Edward Everett of Massachusetts. In Chicago, in May, the Republicans, a coalition of men opposed, in varying degrees, to slavery or its extension, met in their second national convention and nominated Abraham Lincoln of Illinois and Hannibal Hamlin of Maine. Less known than other candidates, Lincoln was regarded as a moderate on the slavery question and ran on a platform which, by opposing the extension of slavery and advocating a homestead law and a protective tariff, appealed to both the agricultural Midwest and the industrial East. Under the tension of the times the traditional two-party system broke down, and a candidate who received a minority of the popular votes cast would be elected President. The Currier and Ives cartoon depicts the plight of the divided Democratic Party.

4. LINCOLN'S ELECTION TRIGGERS SECESSION MOVEMENTS

"The First Flag of Independence Raised in the South, by the Citizens of Savannah, Ga. November 8th, 1860." Lithograph by R. H. Howell, Savannah, Ga., after Henry Cleenewerck. (*See illustration.*) P

Secession as a theory and right had been advocated since the beginnings of the Nation. In New England, in 1814, and in South Carolina, in 1832 and 1852, threats of withdrawal from the Union had been made.

Controversy over the Compromise of 1850 had led to the Nashville convention of Southern States, and by 1860 it was widely regarded that the election of a Republican administration would be the signal for an overt and widespread secession movement. Many Southerners feared that the election of Lincoln would constitute a direct and genuine threat to their rights; others reluctantly believed that regional interests could be better served out of the Union than in it; a strident minority, who had long advocated secession, welcomed the election as the impetus which could lead to Southern independence. On November 6, Abraham Lincoln was elected President of the United States, and popular excitement and secession sentiment were brought to a high pitch throughout the defiant South. This lithograph depicts a meeting protesting Lincoln's election, held in Savannah, Ga., on November 8, at which the first flag of Southern independence was flown.

5. "THE UNION IS DISSOLVED"

"Charleston Mercury Extra: Passed unanimously at 1:15 o'clock, p.m., December 20th, 1860. An ordinance to dissolve the Union between the State of South Carolina and other States united with her under the compact titled 'The Constitution of the United States of America'." [Charleston, S.C., 1860]. Broadside. (*See illustration.*) From the Alfred Whital Stern Collection. R

Propelled by the efforts of such men as Robert Barnwell Rhett, editor of the Charleston *Mercury*, and William Lowndes Yancey of Alabama—"fire-eaters" who had long worked for secession—the South moved swiftly. On December 6 the people of South Carolina voted for delegates to a convention whose decision was a foregone conclusion. "The only questions," an observer wrote, "are *when* shall she secede, and *what* she shall then do." Driven from Columbia by a threat of a smallpox epidemic, the convention assembled in Charleston on December 18, as blue cockades, the emblem of secession,

2

appeared in hats everywhere. Early in the afternoon of December 20, at a session of the convention held in St. Andrew's Hall, a committee reported the ordinance of secession. At 1:15 p.m. the ordinance was passed— yeas 169, nays none. That evening at Institute Hall the engrossed copy was signed by every member of the convention, and David Flavel Jamison, president of the convention, announced: "I proclaim the State of South Carolina an independent Commonwealth." Within minutes of its passage the ordinance appeared as a *Mercury* extra, a copy of which is displayed.

6. THE CONFEDERACY INAUGURATES A PRESIDENT

Jefferson Davis. *Inaugural Address of President Davis, Delivered at the Capitol, Monday, February 18, 1861, at 1 o'clock, p.m.* Montgomery, Ala., 1861.   R

Compromise measures advanced in Congress were rejected by extremists, both North and South, and the formation of the Confederate States of America began. With some opposition from minorities who doubted the expediency, but not the right, of secession, conventions in six States followed South Carolina in withdrawing from the Union: Mississippi, Florida, and Alabama on January 9, 10, and 11, Georgia on January 19, Louisiana on January 26, and, on February 1, Texas, despite the opposition of Governor Sam Houston. Delegates from each of these States, except Texas, where the ordinance had yet to be ratified by a popular vote, met in Montgomery, Ala., on February 4. Calling themselves the Provisional Congress, this body elected Howell Cobb of Georgia as its president, and on February 8 it adopted a provisional constitution, modelled upon that of the United States but with some differences, notably a provision for the protection of the interstate rights of slaveholders. The next day this congress unanimously elected Jefferson Davis of Mississippi as President and Alexander H. Stephens of Georgia

as Vice President. Davis, a former Secretary of War, had left his seat in the United States Senate less than 3 weeks before to accept a military command with Mississippi troops and was at his home, "Brierfield," when he received notification of his election. Reluctantly abandoning his desire for a military career, he set out for Montgomery, where he was introduced by William L. Yancey with the sentence, "The hour and the man have met." On February 18, before cheering thousands, he delivered his inaugural address and took the oath of office. In his address, the President of the new nation was less belligerent than other Southern spokesmen, but few could doubt his determination to maintain the independence of the Confederacy:

We have entered upon the career of independence, and it must be inflexibly pursued. Through many years of controversy with our late associates of the Northern States, we have vainly endeavored to secure tranquillity and obtain respect for the rights to which we were entitled. As a necessity, not a choice, we have resorted to the remedy of separation, and henceforth our energies must be directed to the conduct of our own affairs and the perpetuity of the Confederacy which we have formed. If a just perception of mutual interest should permit us peaceably to pursue our separate political career, my most earnest desire will have been fulfilled. But if this be denied to us and the integrity of our territory and jurisdiction be assailed, it will but remain for us with firm resolve to appeal to arms and invoke the blessing of Providence in a just cause. . . .

7. INAUGURATION OF LINCOLN

"Reading Copy" of the first inaugural address, March 4, 1861. Seven-page printed document, with corrections and insertions in Lincoln's hand. From the Robert Todd Lincoln Collection.   MSS

On February 11, 1861, Abraham Lincoln left his home in Springfield, Ill., to journey to the capital of the divided Nation he had been elected to head. The President-elect had been publicly silent concerning his intentions and policy, and his inaugural address was anxiously awaited. On March 4, reading from the copy exhibited, while riflemen watched from Capitol windows to forestall any attempt upon his life, Lincoln delivered the long-awaited address. He reminded his "dissatisfied fellow countrymen" of his statement that "I have no purpose, directly or indirectly, to interfere with the institution of slavery in the States where it exists." But on secession he was firm: "I . . . consider that, in view of the Constitution and the laws, the Union is unbroken; and, to the extent of my ability, I shall take care, as the Constitution itself expressly enjoins upon me, that the laws of the Union be faithfully executed in all the States. Doing this I deem to be only a simple duty on my part . . . . I trust this will not be regarded as a menace, but only as the declared purpose of the Union that it *will* constitutionally defend, and maintain itself." Further, he added in a significant sentence, "The power confided to me, will be used to hold, occupy, and possess the property, and places belonging to the government. . . ." The message ended with an eloquent, emotional paragraph: "I am loth to close. We are not enemies, but friends. We must not be enemies. Though passion may have strained, it must not break our bonds of affection. The mystic chords of memory, stretching from every battle-field, and patriot grave, to every living heart and hearthstone, all over this broad land, will yet swell the chorus of the Union, when again touched, as surely they will be, by the better angels of our nature." The address was regarded by the Southern press as a declaration of war and a confirmation of their fears of Federal aggression and coercion. The Charleston *Mercury* mentioned the "insolence" and "brutality" of the new President of what it called "a mobocratic Empire," and asked for a policy of "war strategy." Press comment in the North was divided, largely upon political lines. The Hartford *Courant* thought: "The whole civilized world will . . . agree that it is fair to both sides, and worthy of a patriot statesman." The Chicago *Times,* however, termed the message "a loose, disjointed, rambling affair"

and described the Union as "lost beyond hope."

8. CRISIS IN CHARLESTON HARBOR

"Fort Moultrie, Charleston Harbor." Watercolor by "A. Vizitelly," 1861. (*See illustration.*)   P

The focal point of the tension between the North and the South lay, unfortunately, in an area where feelings and passions ran highest. In the harbor of Charleston, S.C., stood Fort Sumter, one of the few Southern forts still remaining in Federal hands. A symbol of national authority, regarded as an affront to the independence and sovereignty of South Carolina and the Confederacy, the fort with its tiny garrison commanded by Maj. Robert Anderson presented an inescapable dilemma which had to be faced by authorities of both governments. As a sovereign nation, the Confederacy could not permit another nation to occupy a fort in a Confederate harbor. On the other hand, for the Federal Government to submit to demands for evacuation would be recognition of the independence of the new nation and an admission that the Union was irrevocably dissolved. In December, Anderson had withdrawn his command of 68 men to Sumter from Fort Moultrie, also in Charleston Harbor. Here these representatives of Federal authority (or Federal coercion, depending upon the point of view) remained while supplies dwindled. A relief ship, *The Star of the West,* was fired upon by South Carolina batteries; and efforts at compromise, negotiation, and mediation failed. When the alternatives were reduced to immediate evacuation of the fort or starvation for Anderson's command, Lincoln, on April 6, notified Governor Francis W. Pickens of South Carolina that "an attempt will be made to supply Fort Sumpter [sic] with provisions only . . . if such attempt be not resisted, no effort to throw in men, arms, or amunition [sic] will be made. . . ." To the authorities in Charleston and Montgomery this was conclusive evidence that the administration in Washington had determined to hold the fort indefinitely—to them an unthinkable situation. Shown is an original watercolor depicting South Carolina militia in Fort Moultrie and, in the harbor, Fort Sumter.

9. THE FIRST SHOT IS FIRED

Holograph diary of Edmund Ruffin, opened to two-page entry for April 12, 1861. From the Ruffin Papers.   MSS

On April 10, the Secretary of War of the Confederate States, Leroy P. Walker, telegraphed Gen. Pierre Gustave Toutant Beauregard, in command of the Confederate forces confronting Fort Sumter: "If you have no doubt of the authorized character of the agent who communicated to you the intention of the Washington Government to supply Fort Sumter by force, you will at once demand its evacuation, and, if this is refused, proceed in such manner as you may determine to reduce it." The next day began an exchange of meticulously formal and correct correspondence between Beauregard and Anderson, who had been his teacher at West Point, in which surrender was courteously demanded and just as courteously refused. The final note was dated April 12, 3:20 a.m. and was carried to Anderson by Beauregard's aides, Col. James Chestnut and Capt. Stephen D. Lee: "By authority of Brigadier General Beauregard, commanding the Provisional Forces of the Confederate States, we have the honor to notify you that he will open the fire of his batteries on Fort Sumter in one hour after this time . . . ." Precisely at 4:30 a.m., a shot arched over the fort. Thirty-four hours later, Anderson surrendered. Ironically, in the long bombardment which ushered in the bloodiest war in American history, no man was killed on either side. Claim to firing the first cannon at Sumter was taken by Edmund Ruffin, a venerable Virginia agriculturist who had enthusiastically aligned himself with South Carolina. In the entry from his diary, which is exhibited, Ruffin records the event:

Before 4 A.M. the drums beat for parade, & our company was speedily on the march to the batteries which they were to man. At 4:30 a signal shell was thrown from a mortar battery at Fort Johnson, which had been before ordered to be taken as the command for immediate attack—& the firing from all the batteries bearing on Fort Sumter next began in the order arranged—which was that the discharges should be two minutes apart, & the round of all the pieces & batteries to be completed in 32 minutes, & then to begin again. The night before, when expecting to engage, Capt. Cuthbert had notified me that his company requested of me to discharge the first cannon to be fired which was their 64 lb. Columbiad, loaded with shell. Of course I was highly gratified by the compliment, & delighted to perform the service—which I did. The shell struck the fort at the north-east angle of the parapet. The firing then proceeded . . .

FORMATION OF THE ARMIES

Twenty-three States with 22 million people supported the Union against 11 States with 9 million people, of whom 3½ million were slaves. From these the rival governments raised the greatest armies the Western Hemisphere had yet seen. Regular forces were small and volunteering was the greatest single means of recruitment, but as enthusiasm waned and casualty lists mounted, conscription was resorted to, though with less than complete success. State, rather than national, agencies undertook recruiting activities, and their efforts, by modern standards, were inefficient, uncoordinated, and haphazard. The maximum size of the contending forces is almost impossible to ascertain because of inadequate and misleading statistics. One estimate, allowing for re-enlistments and varying lengths of service, puts the Union figure at approximately 1½ million, the Confederate at 1 million. A study of men actually

5

on the rolls at any given time puts the Confederate high in January 1864, with 445,000; the Union maximum was reached in January 1865, with 960,000.

10. LINCOLN CALLS FOR TROOPS

Proclamation Calling Militia and Convening Congress, issued by Abraham Lincoln, April 15, 1861. Two-page holograph draft, with interlineations. From the Robert Todd Lincoln Collection.　　　　MSS

Fort Sumter surrendered on April 13. The next morning, a Sunday, Lincoln met with his Cabinet and military officers and drafted this proclamation, in which he invoked a power given to the President in 1795 under which he could call into service the militia of the States to meet "combinations too powerful to be suppressed by the ordinary course of judicial proceedings, or by the powers vested in the Marshals by law." In this document the President called for 75,000 militia to serve for 90 days "in order to suppress said combinations, and to cause the laws to be duly executed," and also set July 4 as the date of a special meeting of Congress. The proclamation had results, immediate and dramatic. In the North, where once there had been many who felt the "erring sisters" should be allowed to go in peace, the firing on Fort Sumter had apparently joined the people in a determination to save the Union. To the people of the upper South, still clinging to the Union, the call for militia was coercion. On April 17, Virginia, by a convention vote of 103 to 46, seceded, to be followed in quick succession by Arkansas, Tennessee, and North Carolina.

11. ROBERT E. LEE MAKES A CHOICE

Two-page holograph letter from Robert E. Lee to Lt. Roger Jones, April 20, 1861. (*See illustration.*) From the Lee Papers.　　MSS

Secession presented thousands of men with an agonizing test of loyalties. In what has been called "a Brother's War," brother did indeed fight against brother, and father against son. The alternatives of choosing between their State or their nation were peculiarly difficult for the officers of the Regular Army and Navy. Many officers in both services resigned their commissions. Generally speaking, the resignations, usually from ranks below that of colonel, came from officers of Southern backgrounds. There were exceptions—George H. Thomas, of Virginia, became one of the most capable of Union generals; Josiah Gorgas, a Pennsylvanian, performed brilliantly in the Confederate Ordnance Bureau. The bitter choice of Col. Robert E. Lee, a Virginian with no sympathy for secession, who 2 days earlier had refused an offer to command the Federal armies, symbolizes the difficult decision which men were forced to make. In this letter he explains his reasons for resigning a commission he had held since 1829:

Sympathizing with you in the troubles that are pressing so heavily upon our beloved Country, & entirely agreeing with you in your notions of allegiance &c., I have been unable to make up my mind to raise my hand against my native State, my relations, my children & my home. I have therefore resigned my Commission in the Army & never desire again to draw my sword save in defense of my State.

12. RECRUITING BY STATES—TEXAS REGIMENTS FOR LEE

Single-page letter from Robert E. Lee to Lewis T. Wigfall, September 21, 1862. From the Wigfall Papers.　　MSS

Volunteer forces, actually State units raised by local effort and accepted into national service, comprised the overwhelming majorities of the armies. Authorities in Washington or in Richmond (to which the Confederate capital was shifted in May), formally empowered by the Congresses to increase the sizes of the armies, issued calls for troops to serve for varying lengths of time. Quotas were assigned to the several States, and the means of recruiting were left to State and municipal authorities. In the letter displayed, Robert E. Lee, now com-

6

manding the Army of Northern Virginia, urges Lewis T. Wigfall, who represented Texas in both the United States and Confederate Senates, to send his army more regiments from his State:

I have not yet heard from you with regard to the new Texas Regiments which you promised to endeavour to raise for this army. I need them much. I rely upon these we have in all tight places and fear I have to call upon them too often. They have fought grandly, nobly, and we must have more of them. Please make every possible exertion to get them in and send them on to me. . . . With a few more such regiments as those which Hood now has, as an example of daring and bravery, I could feel much more confident of the results of the campaign.

13. CONSCRIPTION IN THE CONFEDERACY

Joseph E. Brown. *Correspondence Between Governor Brown and President Davis, on the Constitutionality of the Conscription Act.* Atlanta, Ga., 1862.   R

On April 16, 1862, upon the recommendation of President Davis, the Confederate Congress passed the first Conscription Act in American history. In March of the following year, the Federal Congress also established a draft. Originally, Confederate males between the ages of 18 and 35 were liable to service; the limit was soon raised to 45 and, in the waning months of the war, changed to include men from 17 to 50. The Union age-limits were 18 to 35, with unmarried men up to 45 also liable. Neither conscription was completely successful; on both sides men took fradulent advantage of the exemptions written into the laws; and the practice of hiring substitutes, permitted by both acts, or of paying money in lieu of service led to great dissatisfaction, corruption, and the frequent comment that it was "a rich man's war and a poor man's fight." Conscription was also regarded as a usurpation by the National Government of rights and functions which properly belonged to the States. In conscription President Davis

met the opposition of such governors as Joseph E. Brown of Georgia and Zebulon Vance of North Carolina, who believed it unconstitutional and unwise and at times obstructed its operation. Shown is a contemporary printing of the pertinent correspondence between Governor Brown and President Davis.

14. TYPICAL RECRUITING BROADSIDES

(1) "Freemen! Avoid Conscription! . . . [Signed] S. M. Dennison, of the Confederate States Army. Charleston, Tenn., June 30, 1862."; (2) "To Arms! Rally for the Right! Recruits Wanted for Three Months Service, in Company A, Gray Reserves, Capt. Charles S. Smith . . . Philadelphia [May 26, 1862]." *(See illustration.)*   R

A stigma was attached to conscription, and perhaps the chief value of the draft laws was the stimulus they gave to voluntary enlistments. But the draft, both North and South, acquired mercenary overtones which inevitably led to corruption. Bounties offered to encourage enlistments attracted the bounty jumper, who would enlist in a regiment, collect his bounty, desert, and reenlist in another regiment to repeat the process. The bounty and substitute broker made an unsavory business of furnishing men to the armies. It has been estimated that the Federal and the Northern State governments, in the last 2 years of the war, spent nearly $600 million in bounties, largely to mitigate the effects of conscription, which during the same period produced only 50,000 men but nearly three times as many substitutes. A conservative Confederate estimate puts at 50,000, almost the size of Lee's force in the fall of 1863, the number of men who purchased exemption from service. The majority of the men who served their nations, however, were volunteers, and appeals to enlist, such as these two directed to the peoples of Jefferson and Hawkins Counties, Tenn., and Philadelphia, Pa., were issued throughout the war.

7

15. VOLUNTEERS RESPOND TO LINCOLN'S CALL

"President Lincoln and General Scott Reviewing a Three-Years Regiment on Pennsylvania Avenue." Drawing in pencil and Chinese white by Alfred R. Waud, 1861.   P

In his call for troops Lincoln had stated that "the first service assigned to the forces hereby called . . . will probably be to re-possess the forts, places, and property which have been seized from the Union." In effect, their first duty would be to insure the safety of Washington. When the Sixth Massachusetts was attacked by Southern sympathizers while passing through Baltimore, and the promised regiments failed to arrive, the city, on the edge of the Confederacy, was almost defenseless. In these tense days Lincoln was heard to say, "There is no North," and to ask, "why don't they come?" By May, however, the troops had arrived; the threat had temporarily passed; and Washington began to acquire the military look it would bear throughout the war. The drawing depicts Lincoln and the aging Winfield Scott, commander of the United States armies, reviewing a regiment of three-year volunteers in 1861, probably in the early summer.

16. CONFEDERATES RALLY TO THE CAUSE

"The Civil War in America: the Confederate Army—Mississippians Passing in Review Before General Beauregard and Staff." Photocopy of wood engraving in *The Illustrated London News*, December 14, 1861. (*See illustration.*)   P

In March 1861, the Confederate Congress authorized President Davis to accept 100,000 volunteers for 12 months. An additional 400,000 were authorized on August 8. In July, an estimated 112,000 men were on the rolls of the Confederate army, and Secretary of War Walker informed the President that if arms could be furnished "no less than 200,000 additional volunteers for the war could be found in our ranks in less than two months." The Secretary was almost right, for, in the enthusiasm of the times, the July figure was more than tripled by the end of the year. Volunteer forces from Mississippi being reviewed by Beauregard are depicted in this woodcut.

SOLDIER'S LIFE

The enlisted man, the anonymous hero of all wars, bore the burdens of the struggle. For causes they believed right and just (or for adventure, or, sometimes, because they were forced to) "Johnny Reb" and "Billy Yank" faced dangers and hardships, privations and monotony, irksome duties and disciplines which were remarkably similar. Although the Union forces were generally much better supplied, soldiers of both armies were alike in their concern with food and shelter, recreation, and the desire to make the best of an unusual and uncomfortable situation until they could get home again.

17. SOME FACES FROM THE WAR

Photocopies of ambrotypes and tintypes. Photographers not determined.   P

The soldiers came from widely diverse backgrounds and occupations. A few were very young and some were very old, but the bulk of both armies probably came from the 18-to-35 age-group. A majority of the Confederate army and a large percentage of the Union forces were farmers; many on both sides were foreign-born. Shown are photographs of six enlisted men: Pvt. Walter

Parker, 1st Florida Cavalry, CSA; Pvt. Harrison Corbin, Company G, 34th Pennsylvania Infantry, killed at Fredericksburg; Pvt. Phillip Carper, White's 35th Battalion, Virginia Cavalry, CSA; Sgt. Joshua P. Graffam, Company L, 1st District of Columbia Cavalry; Pvt. Edwin Francis Jennison, of a Georgia regiment, killed at Malvern Hill (*see frontispiece*); and an unknown Union soldier from a New York regiment.

18. FOOD FOR UNION VOLUNTEERS

"Commissary Department. Encampment of the Mass. 6th Regiment of Volunteers at the Relay House Near Baltimore, Md., 1861." Lithograph by J. H. Bufford, Boston, 1861, after Alfred Ordway. (*See illustration.*)
P

Food was of first importance, and letters from soldiers of both armies seldom fail to mention it. The Union soldier usually complained that he could not eat what was available; the Confederate's grievance was that often there was nothing available. Herds of cattle, to be slaughtered for fresh beef, sometimes accompanied the armies, but the staples of the ration were dried and preserved provisions: "salt horse and hardtack" (salt beef and a thick, incredibly hard cracker), dried beans, rice, corn meal, and "dessicated" vegetables. Supplies for the Union armies were not always as efficiently distributed as this lithograph, made early in in the war, would lead one to believe.

19. CONFEDERATE RATIONS

Headquarters, Army of Tennessee, Dalton, Ga., Jan. 23, 1864. Single-page manuscript circular ("Table of Rations"). From the Confederate Miscellany Collection. MSS

The Confederate soldier often suffered great hardships from hunger, especially when campaigning in regions removed from food-producing areas. Shortages began early in the war and became more pronounced,

especially in Virginia, as the supply and transportation systems broke down. There were also wide discrepancies between what a soldier was authorized as a ration and what he actually received. This "table of rations," which directs that from Feb. 1, 1864, "beef, meal, rice or peas, sugar, soap, salt, vinegar & grits will constitute the regular daily issue until otherwise ordered," is not necessarily indicative of what other Confederate armies were being issued.

20. CONFEDERATES COOKING IN THE FIELD

Photograph probably by J. D. Edwards, 1861.
P

Food was prepared sometimes by company cooks. More often in the field individual soldiers or small informal groups cooked their own rations. From necessity and ingenuity unusual dishes developed. "Cush," for example, a Confederate concoction, was a mixture of bacon grease, cold beef, water, and crumbled corn bread, mixed in a skillet. Both armies came to know that an order to prepare 3 days' rations in advance was an indication that a battle was imminent. The photograph shows members of Company B of the 9th Mississippi Infantry, encamped at Pensacola, Fla., preparing food over an open fire.

21. MESS CALL IN A UNION CAMP

"The Army of the Potomac—Drawing Rations." Photocopy of wood engraving in *Harper's Weekly*, August 22, 1863, after Thomas Nast.
P

Food in camp, as this illustration indicates, was customarily prepared in large iron kettles (of varying sizes, so that one could be placed inside the other when the army was on the move). Such staples as potatoes and meat, when these were available, were cooked either in separate pots or cut up and cooked together to form a stew. Food and hot coffee were served in tin plates and cups carried by the men to the line which formed when the order to "fall in for rations" was given.

22. FORAGING

"Roasting Corn" and "Foraging." Unsigned pencil drawings, probably by Arthur Lumley. (*See illustration.*) P

Soldiers of both armies supplemented their monotonous rations by stripping the land of whatever provisions they could find. This practice of living off the land, sometimes with, sometimes against orders, often left the paths of the marching armies bare of foodstuffs and led to occasional excesses against the civilian population. A Confederate wrote that "Our soldiers have not left a fat hog, chicken, turkey, goose, duck, or eggs or onions behind." Foraging, illustrated by these drawings, reached its peak in Sherman's march through Georgia.

23. TENTS IN A SOUTHERN CAMP

"Confederate Camp During the late American War." Chromolithograph by M. & N. Hanhart, London, 1871, after a painting by Conrad Wise Chapman, 59th Virginia Regiment, Wise's Brigade. P

In the field, when conditions permitted, soldiers made themselves as comfortable as possible. At least three types of tents, represented here, were in use throughout the war. These were the "Sibley," large and conical, supported by a center pole and capable of accommodating 12 men; the wedge tent, an inverted "V" of canvas, supported by a ridgepole resting on two vertical poles and capable of sleeping six; and the wall tent, with four upright sides. Chapman's romanticized image of this Confederate camp near Corinth, Miss., set among moss-festooned oaks and pines, is illustrative of the observation that Confederate camps were likely to be found in wooded areas, Union camps in open spaces.

During the period 1862–64, painter Conrad Wise Chapman, who had studied under his father, noted artist John Gadsby Chapman, was a member of the 59th Virginia regiment, where he held the rank of ordnance sergeant. His war paintings include portraits of Confederate officers and soldiers, views of camp life, and a series of paintings of the defenses of Charleston Harbor, made in 1863, and now in the Confederate Museum in Richmond.

24. HOLED UP FOR THE WINTER

Soldiers' Huts in Winter Camp Near Fredericksburg, Va., Feb. 12, 1863. Pencil drawing by Edwin Forbes. P

Like food, clothing, and equipment, shelter (especially during the winter months) was a matter of primary concern to the soldier. Both armies on occasion made log huts, such as these which were used for the quartering of Federal troops after the battle of Fredericksburg. Built of rough logs, mortared with mud, roofed with sod or brush, and now and then having barrels for chimneys, these structures had their drawbacks but were much more comfortable than tents and could be built in a few hours.

25. TEMPORARY SHELTER FOR PICKETS

"Ravine Occupied by the Picket Reserves of Brig. Gen. Joseph Hooker's Division, Heintzelman's Corps D'Armee, at the Siege of Yorktown, April, 1862." Colored lithograph by Endicott & Co., New York, 1862, after John B. Bachelder. P

Bivouacked in brush-covered lean-tos during a phase of the Peninsular campaign, these members of a Union detail are waiting to serve as sentinels. Soldiers in both armies performed picket duty, manning advance outposts to prevent the main body of troops from being taken by surprise.

26. DAILY DUTIES IN CAMP

Head-Quarters, Army of Tennessee, Dalton, Ga., Jan. 8, 1864. General Orders, no. 5. Seven-page printed document. From the Confederate Miscellany Collection.   MSS

When he was not fighting, or marching, or working, the soldier of the Civil War was likely to be training, and, as with soldiers everywhere, his time was not his own. In camp in northwestern Georgia, Gen. Joseph E. Johnston issued an order outlining a day from reveille at daylight to taps at 9 p.m., which was probably much like days in other armies, both Union and Confederate. The first page begins:

Head-Quarters, Army of Tennessee,
Dalton, Ga., Jan. 8, 1864.

General Orders, No. 5.

I. The following regulations are published for the government of the troops of this army in camp. They are to be read at the head of each company at least once every week. Copies are to be furnished all field, staff and company officers:

1st. The hours of service and roll call as follows:

Reveille_____	At day-light.
Police_____	Immediately after reveille.
Surgeon's Call_____	Fifteen minutes after reveille.
Stable Call_____	Fifteen minutes after reveille.
First Sergeant's Call.	Half hour after reveille.
Breakfast_____	At sunrise.
Adjutant's Call____	At 9 a.m.
Drill_____	From 10 to 11½ a.m.
Officer's Drill_____	From 11 a.m. to 12 m.
Dinner_____	At 12½ p.m.
Drill_____	From 2½ to 4 p.m.
Guard Mounting___	At 4 p.m.
Stable Call_____	At 4 p.m.
Camp and Company Police.	At 4½ p.m.
Dress Parade_____	At sunset.
Supper_____	Immediately after parade.
Tattoo_____	At 8 p.m.
Taps_____	One hour after tattoo.

27. ENDLESS HOURS OF DRILL

(1) Headquarters, 2d Brigade, Camp at Valley Mills, April 23, 1862. Singe-page manuscript circular; (2) Headquarters, Army of Northern Virginia, Camp at Valley Mills, May 3, 1862. Single-page manuscript circular. From the Jedediah Hotchkiss Papers.   MSS

Officers of both armies faced the task of converting enthusiastic civilians into disciplined soldiers by the traditional methods of drill and inspection. In these circulars Gen. Edward Johnson, commanding a small Confederate force in the Shenandoah Valley, prescribed 4 hours of drill daily, plus inspections and dress parades on Sundays.

28. "HAY FOOT! STRAW FOOT!"

Photograph by Mathew B. Brady or assistant, 1862. (See illustration.)   P

The Union soldier shared his Confederate counterpart's daily drill and training. This photograph of the troops of the 96th Pennsylvania Infantry drilling at Camp Northumberland, near Washington, recalls the army expression, "hay foot! straw foot!," said to have originated in the instruction camps of the Civil War. Foreign-born soldiers, unable to understand English, were sometimes drilled with wisps of straw and hay tied to their shoes to distinguish the right foot from the left.

29. ARTILLERY DRILL IN THE UNION ARMY

Photograph by unidentified photographer.   P

The complex maneuvering necessary to place in position and fire cannon required many hours of training. In addition to his own responsibilities, each man was also expected to be able to perform in an emergency the duties of the other men in the squad. The photograph is of Union soldiers going through an intricate drill with a Parrott gun, a rifled muzzle-loading cannon, recognizable by the heavy wrought-iron band around the breech.

30. A CONFEDERATE COURT-MARTIAL

Headquarters First Division, Western Department, Columbus, Ky., December 15, 1861. General Order no. 25. Broadside. From the Confederate Miscellany Collection. MSS

The volunteer soldiers understood little of army regulations and chafed under their restraints. The majority in both armies came to accept the need for discipline, but rules were often broken. Courts-martial were frequent and the punishments often harsh, particularly for desertion. This General Order publishes the findings of a general court-martial which convened at Camp Beauregard, Ky. Of 11 privates tried, three, charged with the crime of desertion (violation of the 20th Article of War), were found guilty. The Court allowed them their lives but sentenced each "to forfeit to the Confederate States all pay and allowances that are now or may become due him; to receive fifty lashes well laid on his bare back with a rawhide; to have branded on his left hip the letter "D"; to have his head shaved, and to be drummed out of the service."

31. AN EXECUTION IN THE FEDERAL ARMY

Two-page handwritten telegram (received copy) from George G. Meade to Abraham Lincoln, Oct. 29, 1863. From the Robert Todd Lincoln Collection. MSS

Desertions in both armies increased as the war progressed and reached incredible totals. Many classed as deserters later returned to their units; others, the "bounty jumpers," deserted and joined other regiments to receive an additional bounty. Often men left their regiments because they were needed at home. The effect of desertion upon morale and discipline became of great concern to military commanders. Court-martial sentences were severe, but the death sentence was seldom carried out in either of the armies. Frequently President Lincoln intervened personally to commute the sentences of Union soldiers. The telegram exhibited is concerned with a case in which intervention came too late.

32. "THE ROGUE'S MARCH"

Photograph by Haas and Peale, July 1863.
P

There was little consistency in sentencing violators of regulations. Punishments varied in severity from regiment to regiment. Sometimes they were brutal; often they were humiliating. Slight offenses might require the culprit to carry a heavy log, or weighted knapsack, or to wear a sign around his neck proclaiming his crime, for prescribed periods of time. More serious breaches of discipline were punished by branding or flogging (forbidden, but often practiced). Tying a man up by his thumbs, or spread-eagling him on a wagon wheel, were common, and severe, punishments. Certain crimes, thievery for example, were punished by stripping the offender of his military insignia and ceremoniously driving him from camp. Illustrated in the photograph is "The Rogue's March," in which a thief is being drummed out of a Union camp at Morris Island, S.C.

33. LEE ON GAMBLING

Headquarters, Army of Northern Virginia, November 14, 1862. General Orders, no. 127. Two-page printed document. From the Jedediah Hotchkiss Papers. MSS

In their personal behavior the soldiers acted much like men in other American wars. The great majority were no better or no worse than other large bodies of men. There were, of course, exceptions. Gambling was common in both armies. In the general order shown, Robert E. Lee expresses his pain in learning that "the vice of gambling exists and is becoming common in this Army."

34. "HALLOA YANK! HALLOA, REB!"

Holograph diary of Lyman D. Holford, Jan. 1–Dec. 31, 1863.   MSS

As the war progressed, soldiers of the contending armies gained a solid respect for those on the opposing side and an understanding that their lives had much in common. They fought each other as fiercely as ever, but occasionally, with a wary eye out for officers, they arranged brief, informal truces. This fraternization usually was between rival pickets, who sometimes met to exchange newspapers or trade coffee and tobacco. The diary of Lyman Holford of the 6th Wisconsin records one of these encounters between young Americans:

This morning [July 1] at 7 o'clock as I was on post one of the rebs saluted me with: Halloa Yank! and notwithstanding orders to the contrary I answered with Halloa, Reb! and from that we got into a conversation which ended in his sending three Richmond papers across the river on a board with a small sail attached, and some of our boys sent some papers back on the same craft—The day was fine as we could wish and taking everything into consideration we have had a good time so far.

35. SOLDIERS ELECT THEIR OFFICERS

Report on the Election of Officers in the 47th Regiment of Virginia Volunteers, May 1, 1862. Single-page manuscript document, signed by George W. Richardson, Colonel Commanding. From the Papers of the Ward Family.   MSS

The practice of letting enlisted men choose their company (and even regimental) officers was common early in the war, and did much to increase the individualism of the private soldier. All too often popularity or influence, rather than military competence, determined the command of units. Discipline was undermined, and men sometimes resented orders from an individual they themselves had chosen as commander. On one occasion a Georgia colonel was ridden on a rail by men of his regiment until "on promise to them of better behavior he was allowed to resume his command." This report concerns the election of William N. Ward, Jr., to the office of first lieutenant in Co. D, 47th Virginia Regiment.

36. RELIGION AMONG THE TROOPS

"Rev. L. F. Drake, Chaplain 31st Ohio Volunteers, Preaching at Camp Dick Robinson, Ky., November 10th, 1861." Lithograph by Middleton, Strobridge & Co., Cincinnati, after A. E. Mathews, 31st Regt., O.V. (*See illustration.*)   P

Both armies held religious services as regularly as circumstances permitted. The services were often held in the open, sometimes at night, by the chaplains who accompanied the armies or by a local minister. Services at this Union camp in Kentucky apparently were open to soldiers and civilians alike.

37. A CONFEDERATE HYMNAL

The Army Hymn-Book. Richmond, Va., 1864.   R

The Confederate army underwent a period of revivalism in 1863–1864 which persisted throughout the remainder of the war. A part of the cause of this phenomenon is probably the success of various denominations and Bible and tract societies in providing religious literature to the soldiers. One of the most popular of pocket-sized booklets distributed to the army was this little hymnal. Published by the Presbyterian Church, it first appeared in 1863.

38. A CONFEDERATE GENERAL PRAYS

"Prayer in Stonewall Jackson's Camp." Etching no. 24 in Adalbert J. Volck's *Confederate War Etchings* ([Baltimore(?), 18—]).   R

A staunch Presbyterian, Gen. Thomas J. ("Stonewall") Jackson was known for his piety as well as for his abilities as a leader. In this drawing by Baltimore artist Adalbert

J. Volck, he stands at the left, a bearded figure leading the men in devotions, his hands folded in prayer.

39. RECREATION IN A UNION ARMY CAMP

"Camp of the 37th Mass. Vol's. Near Brandy Station, Va." Lithograph by J. H. Bufford, Boston.   P

Soldiers of a Massachusetts regiment gather at the edge of camp to engage in a few favorite diversions—leapfrog, ball-and-bat games, cards, and tall tales.

40. ENTERTAINMENT IN A REBEL CAMP

"Night Amusements in the Confederate Camp." Photocopy of wood engraving in *The Illustrated London News,* Jan. 10, 1863, after Frank Vizetelly.   P

Some organized efforts, such as amateur theatricals and concerts, were made to entertain the soldiers, but the diversions of camp life were largely spontaneous and unorganized. In the field, as artist-correspondent Vizetelly shows, the campfire was the center of social life. Here the men gathered to entertain themselves. This particular camp, Vizetelly reports, was fortunate enough to possess Sweeny (here portrayed), "the most famous banjo-player in the Southern States". The Negro doing a jig is probably a slave who had accompanied his master to the war. As the Federal armies advanced, and supplies dwindled, this practice decreased.

41. A CARD GAME IN THE TRENCHES

"The Interrupted Game. Within the Intrenchments Before Petersburg." Lithograph by J. Mayer & Co., Boston, 1864.   P

Playing cards were often thrown away when action seemed imminent; the soldiers, possibly fearing divine wrath, preferred not to carry them into battle. The monotony of the long stalemate before Petersburg led some men, apparently, to overlook this precaution. This lithograph, showing cards and players scattered by a shell which has landed in the trenches, also provides a view of the "bomb proofs" which soldiers constructed as trench warfare became more prevalent in the closing years of the war.

42. NEWSPAPERS IN CAMP

"Papers in Camp. Near Rappahannock Station, Sept. 18th, 1863." Pencil drawing by Edwin Forbes.   P

News from home and news on the progress of the war were eagerly read by the soldiers. Such is the "feeling" of this scene, showing the arrival of papers from Washington at a Union camp in Virginia.

43. OUR NATIONAL GAME IN THE SIXTIES

"Union Prisoners at Salisbury, N.C." Colored lithograph by Sarony, Major & Knapp, New York, 1863, after Otto Boetticher.   P

Baseball, popular even before 1861, was given great impetus by the Civil War. Played behind the lines whenever possible, it then was widely disseminated by soldiers after their demobilization. This lithograph shows Union soldiers playing the game in a Confederate prison camp at Salisbury, N.C. As pictured here, the game apparently was quite similar to present-day softball; no gloves are in use, and the pitcher is throwing underhand.

Artist Otto Boetticher, an officer of the 68th New York Volunteer Infantry, had before the war maintained a studio in New York City, where he produced lithographs on military subjects. In the spring of 1862 he was captured and imprisoned at Salisbury, where he drew the celebrated scene displayed. Later in the year he was exchanged and in 1865 was brevetted lieutenant-colonel for gallant and meritorious conduct.

44. MUSIC FOR THE FEDERAL TROOPS

Photograph by unidentified photographer, Washington, D.C., Apr. 1865.　　P

A Mississippian's diary describes the regimental band as "a great institution. It . . . labors with the greatest assiduity at 'tooting.' Their music, however, is never the sweetest nor most harmonious." Organized bands, such as that of the 10th Veteran Reserve Corps, USA, shown here, were much more common in the Union Army than in the Confederate. These units provided music for drill and gave occasional evening concerts for the recreation of the troops.

45. A CIVIL WAR "POST EXCHANGE"

Photograph by James F. Gibson, Feb. 1864.　　P

Sutlers were civilians who followed the armies, selling small items not otherwise available to the soldiers. Among the goods they sold (for exorbitant prices) were cakes and small pies, canned fruit, writing supplies, playing cards, and illegal whiskey. The sutler, his wagon, and tent were familiar sights, especially on paydays, when he sometimes claimed a large amount of the private's salary of $14 a month. The photograph shows the tent of "A. Foulke, Sutler," at the headquarters of the 1st Brigade, Horse Artillery, Brandy Station, Va.

46. JOHNNY REB APPLIES FOR LEAVE

"Army of the Confederate States. Certificate of Disability for Furlough." Broadside form, filled in. From the Jubal A. Early Papers.　　MSS

On April 14, 1862, a Confederate private, W. A. Barrett, of the 23d North Carolina Regiment, stationed near Yorktown, Va., and suffering from a fractured clavicle, filled out this application for leave. Despite an examination at the Chimborazo Hospital in Richmond and a doctor's recommendation of "a furlough for him for 30 days," Barrett's commanding officers, in endorsements on the reverse of the form, "disapproved" his request.

47. OBSEQUIES IN A CAMP CEMETERY

"Soldiers Burial." Colored lithograph by Gibson & Co., Cincinnati.　　P

From casualties in battle and disease, the war cost the lives of over half a million Americans. Of this grim casualty total, more than half came about through disease, which spread rapidly under camp conditions. A correspondent describing a camp near Manassas wrote: "The saddest of all things connected with soldier life are the deaths and burials in camp. . . . Every day we hear the muffled drums, and see the solemn march, with reversed arms, and hear the rattling musketry." Under battle conditions even the simple ceremony depicted here often did not take place.

THE WAR ON THE LAND

The summer of 1861 ended for both sides the prospect of a quick and easy war, and the remainder of the year was largely spent in raising, training, and equipping armies for the struggle ahead. With some exceptions, Federal successes through 1863 were confined to the West, Confederate victories to the East. In the early months of 1862, engagements at Fort Henry, Fort Donelson, and Shiloh in Tennessee and Pea Ridge in Arkansas had made Kentucky and Missouri secure to the Union and put Western Tennessee under Federal control. The fall of New Orleans in April 1862, and Vicksburg in July 1863, split the

Confederacy. In the East, where the battlefields were principally in Virginia, the outnumbered, but brilliantly led, Confederate forces had thwarted attempts to capture Richmond; won resounding victories in the Shenandoah Valley, at First and Second Bull Run, Fredericksburg, and Chancellorsville; and twice, at Antietam and Gettysburg, brought the war to Union soil.

By March 1864, President Lincoln had found his general and Ulysses S. Grant was given command of all the Union armies. Against his strategy of applying unrelenting pressure in all theaters of the war, giving the dwindling Confederate forces no chance to consolidate, Lee fought and maneuvered brilliantly and gallantly, hoping to prolong the war until the Northern public would no longer support it. As Grant moved into Virginia, Sherman moved in Georgia; and despite reversals, at times with terrible losses, held to the design which brought about the surrender of the Confederate armies. War became a matter of endurance, brutal and appallingly modern in its concepts.

48. "THE WAR BEGUN IN EARNEST"

"The Star—Extra. Friday, May 24, 1861— 11 a.m. The War Begun in Earnest. A Midnight March. Movement Upon Alexandria and the Virginia Heights. Brutal Assassination of Col. Ellsworth in Alexandria. A Swift and Terrible Retribution." [Washington, D.C., 1861]. Broadside. From the Alfred Whital Stern Collection.

R

On May 24, 1861, Federal units crossed the Potomac to occupy Alexandria, Va. Elmer E. Ellsworth, commander of a company of Fire Zouaves and a personal friend of President Lincoln, removed a Confederate flag from its staff atop the Marshall House. He was killed by the proprietor, James W. Jackson, who in turn was killed, and North and South had their first martyrs. Within weeks there would be many more, and the war would be far more in earnest.

49. MILITARY LEADERS OF THE CONFEDERACY

"Lee and His Generals." Lithograph by Tholey, published by John Smith, Philadelphia, 1867. (*See illustration.*) P

Much of the success of the outnumbered, poorly equipped Confederate armies lay in the brilliance and spirit of their individual commanders. The lithograph shows Robert E. Lee, who for most of the war commanded the Army of Northern Virginia, surrounded by some of his generals. In the foreground, on horseback, are Beauregard, Joseph E. Johnston, Lee, and Jackson.

50. WHITE HOUSE REACTION TO BULL RUN

Seven-page holograph letter from John G. Nicolay to Therena Bates, July 21, 1861. From the Nicolay Papers. MSS

At Bull Run (or Manassas) the undisciplined and unorganized armies met in what has been described as the war's "best planned and worst fought" battle. Under political pressures and realities (the terms of the 90-day militia would soon expire), Irvin McDowell reluctantly ordered an advance of the Union forces on July 16. On July 21, along a small stream about 30 miles southwest of Washington, thousands of Northern and Southern boys "saw the elephant" (slang for a soldier's first engagement in battle). The outcome was in doubt until late afternoon, when the Confederate forces, led by the hero of Sumter, Pierre G. T. Beauregard, and by Joseph E. Johnston, routed their opponents and sent them streaming back to Washington, preceded by the carriages of Congressmen who had driven out, with picnic-lunches, to witness the battle. John G. Nicolay, the President's secretary, described to his fiancee how the news of the defeat was received in the White House:

At 6 oclock . . . Mr. Seward came into the President's room, with a terribly frightened and excited look, and said . . . "The battle is lost. The telegraph says that McDowell is in full retreat, and calls on General Scott to save the Capitol &c. Find the President and tell him to come immediately to Gen. Scotts." In about half an hour the President came in. We told him, and he started off immediately. John [Hay] and I continued to sit at the windows and could now distinctly hear heavy cannonading on the other side of the river. . . .

51. THE WAR IN THE WEST: FORT DONELSON

"Battle of Fort Donelson." Colored lithograph by Sarony, Major & Knapp, New York, 1862.   P

Fort Donelson, on the banks of the Cumberland River in Tennessee, was the sole obstacle to a Union advance along the entire Confederate line of defense in the West. Successfully resisting attacks by land forces and gunboats on February 13 and 14, 1862, the garrison failed in a counterattack on the following day. That night over 14,000 men surrendered to a stocky Union general, Ulysses S. Grant. His reply to a request for terms became famous in the North: "No terms except unconditional and immediate surrender can be accepted. I propose to move immediately upon your works."

52. JACKSON IN THE SHENANDOAH VALLEY

"Sketch of the Battle of Kernstown, Sunday, March 23d 1862." Manuscript map drawn by Jedediah Hotchkiss, top. eng'r, V.D.   M

At Bull Run, Thomas J. Jackson, once a professor at Virginia Military Institute, was given the sobriquet of "Stonewall" by South Carolinian Barnard E. Bee. In the Shenandoah Valley in the spring of 1862 he gained military immortality by a campaign which critics have regarded as one of the most brilliant in American history. With numerically inferior forces, he succeeded in outwitting, outmarching, and outfighting Union com-

manders in a series of battles. The action symbolized here was one of his rare defeats, but the audacity of his attack so alarmed Washington that it helped him attain his objective of preventing Federal troops from joining the advance upon Richmond. This map of the battlefield at Kernstown, March 23, 1862, was drawn by the noted Confederate cartographer, Jedediah Hotchkiss, at the time on assignment to Jackson's staff as topographical engineer of the Valley District, Department of Virginia.

53. McCLELLAN BUILDS A GREAT ARMY

Photograph by Mathew B. Brady or assistant.   P

To George Brinton McClellan, who had gained Union victories in West Virginia in the summer of 1861, was given the task of training and organizing the Army of the Potomac. Under him this army developed into a magnificent, well-equipped fighting force which was assigned the task of capturing Richmond by moving up the peninsula formed by the York and James Rivers. An able administrator, but not aggressive and inclined to underestimate his own strength and over-estimate the enemy's, McClellan began the campaign by laying siege to Yorktown. (*See also* entry 99.) Here he accumulated vast stores of supplies needed in his ponderous advance toward Richmond. The photograph, probably taken by one of Brady's assistants—possibly James F. Gibson—shows Federal ordnance (mortars and Parrott guns) ready for transportation from Yorktown.

54. THE WAR IN THE WEST: SHILOH

"The Battle of Shiloh. Charge and Taking of a New Orleans Battery by the 14th Regt. Wisconsin Volunteers, Monday, April 7, 1862." Lithograph by Ehrgott, Forbriger & Co., Cincinnati, 1862, after A. E. Mathews, 31st Regt., O.V.   P

In early April Albert Sidney Johnston, commanding the Confederate forces in the West, launched a surprise attack which developed into one of the most savage battles of the war. At Shiloh, or Pittsburg Landing, the Union Army under Ulysses S. Grant was encamped along the Tennessee River near the Mississippi border. Almost overwhelmed by the fury of Johnston's assault, the Federal forces held on with the aid of gunboats until reinforcements arrived. They counterattacked the next day. The Confederate army, exhausted by the violence of its attacks and confused by the death of its commander, withdrew. The cost of the action of April 6 and 7, 1862, was a combined loss of over 24,000 men. (*See also* entry 97.)

55. LEE HALTS McCLELLAN BEFORE RICHMOND

"The Army of the Potomac. The Wagon Trains of the Army of the Potomac en Route from Chickahominy to James River, Va., During the Seven Days' Fight (Fording Bear Creek one mile below Savage Station), June 29th, 1862." Colored lithograph by J. H. Bufford, Boston, 1863, after John B. Bachelder.   P

The controversial Peninsular Campaign began on March 17, 1862, when George B. McClellan, prodded into action by President Lincoln, embarked the Army of the Potomac for Fortress Monroe. From this point, with a superiority in numbers over his opponent, Joseph E. Johnston, which was originally quite large, McClellan inched his way up the peninsula until his outposts were within five miles of Richmond. On May 31, at Fair Oaks, or Seven Pines, Johnston was wounded, and on the following day Robert E. Lee assumed command of a force known thereafter as the Army of Northern Virginia. The first 3 weeks of June were distinguished largely by J. E. B. Stuart's spectacular cavalry reconnaissance, which took a force of 1,000 men 150 miles completely around McClellan's army. With numbers made more nearly equal by the arrival of "Stonewall" Jackson's army from the Shenandoah

Valley, Lee took the offensive and began the famous Seven Days' Battle, which started at Mechanicsville on June 26 and ended at Malvern Hill on July 1. On that night McClellan began the retreat toward his base at Harrison's Landing on the James River. The print exhibited shows the wagon trains of the Army of the Potomac during this withdrawal. The unsuccessful Peninsular Campaign ended on July 11, when Henry W. Halleck, recently appointed General in Chief of the Union Armies, ordered the Army of the Potomac withdrawn. The Confederates had suffered more losses (20,000) than the Federals (15,000) in the long, complex struggle, but the Union Army had failed in its objective, the capture of Richmond.

56. LEE CONGRATULATES THE ARMY OF NORTHERN VIRGINIA

Headquarters, Army of Northern Virginia, October 2, 1862. General Orders, no. 116. Broadside. From the Confederate Miscellany Collection.   MSS

In August Lee moved most of his forces from Richmond and began movements around Manassas. Here, on August 30, the Union Army under a new commander, John Pope, was routed and driven back to Washington. Hopeful of attracting adherents to the Confederate cause, and anxious to carry the war into enemy territory, in early September Lee invaded Maryland. A force under Jackson was detached and captured Harper's Ferry with 11,000 prisoners, and on September 15 the advance had reached Sharpsburg, along Antietam Creek. In the meantime, McClellan (who had been reappointed commander of the Army of the Potomac by President Lincoln in spite of bitter political opposition) had gained, by a lost order, advance knowledge of Lee's movements and used it for victories at South Mountain and Crampton's Gap on September 14, a prelude to the war's most costly day. On September 17, at the indecisive battle of Antietam, or Sharpsburg, the two sides suffered combined losses of over 23,000 men. Lee held his battered lines the next day; McClellan failed to commit fresh troops; and on September 18, the Confederates recrossed the Potomac. On October 2 Lee issued this general order, in which he recapitulated the events of the campaign and thanked the Army of Northern Virginia for the "indomitable courage it has displayed in battle, and its cheerful endurance of privation and hardship, on the march."

57. THE WAR IN THE WEST: KENTUCKY

"Kentuckians! The Army of the Confederate States, Has Again Entered Your Territory Under my Command. [Signed] Kirby Smith, Maj. Gen. C. S. Army." [Sept. (?) 1862]. Broadside.   R

About the time of Lee's movement into Maryland, Edmund Kirby-Smith and Braxton Bragg launched an offensive designed to recover Kentucky for the Confederacy. Meeting with some initial success, the invasion ended at the indecisive battle of Perryville on October 8. The failure of the concerted movements returned the initiative to the Union and insured that for almost the remainder of the war the South would be on the defensive. This broadside calls upon Kentuckians to support the Confederate cause.

58. LINCOLN VISITS THE ARMY OF THE POTOMAC

Photograph by Alexander Gardner, Oct. 3, 1862.   P

After Antietam, McClellan failed to exploit whatever advantage he had gained. Hoping to urge the general to the hard fighting he knew was necessary to end the war, President Lincoln paid a visit to the Army of the Potomac, which he wryly described as "General McClellan's bodyguard." This photograph of the President with McClellan and members of his staff was taken by Gardner near the battlefield of Antietam.

59. UNION VALOR UNSUCCESSFUL AT FREDERICKSBURG

"Bombardment and Capture of Fredericksburg, Va., Dec. 11th 1862." Colored lithograph by Currier & Ives, New York.   P

On November 5, President Lincoln replaced George B. McClellan with Ambrose E. Burnside as the commanding general of the Army of the Potomac. Burnside moved quickly and arrived at Fredericksburg, Va., on the Rappahannock, on November 17. Hampered first by bad weather, he delayed moving until Lee had his army in an almost impregnable position across the river. On December 11 and 12 engineers threw up bridges, and on December 13 the attack began. Moving first across the river, and then advancing over an open space, against Confederates firing from behind a stone wall on Marye's Heights, the Union forces had little chance and were forced to withdraw. They suffered more than 12,000 casualties. A Northern paper commented: "It can hardly be in human nature for men to show more valor, or generals to manifest less judgment."

The lithograph, speaking as it does of the "capture" of Fredericksburg, evidently was rushed into print before the outcome of the battle was certain. Of the many lithographic views of the war (the leading printmakers were situated in Boston, New York, Philadelphia, and Cincinnati), the Currier and Ives battle scenes, of which there are more than 200, were, curiously enough, the most popular with the public but the least notable for accuracy of portrayal.

60. THE WAR IN THE WEST: MURFREESBORO

Six-page telegram (received copy) from William S. Rosecrans to Henry W. Halleck, Jan. 4, 1863. From the Robert Todd Lincoln Collection.   MSS

In the closing days of 1862, the Confederate Army of Tennessee, commanded by Braxton Bragg, was encamped at Murfreesboro, southeast of Nashville (which had been reached by the Union Army of the Cumberland, led by William S. Rosecrans, in November). Rosecrans advanced on December 28, and on December 30 both armies were in sight of each other. The battle began the next day, with the advantage going to Bragg. It was resumed on January 2. That evening Federal reinforcements arrived and Bragg withdrew. Union losses (killed, wounded, and missing) in the 2-day, indecisive engagement were 13,000; Confederate 12,000. Rosecrans in this telegram to General in Chief Henry W. Halleck reporting the battle of Murfreesboro, or Stone River, observes: "This whole country is a natural fortification & worse than Corinth. No great battle can be fought without making regular approaches." (For a lithographic view of action at Stone River, *see* entry 106.)

61. FEDERAL TROOPS MOVE TOWARD DEFEAT AT CHANCELLORSVILLE

Scene on the United States Ford Road at Night. The 2nd and 3rd Corps Marching into the Fight of Chancellorsville, Apr. 30, 1863. Pencil drawing by Edwin Forbes. P

In January 1863, President Lincoln, still seeking a general, appointed Joseph E. Hooker to the command of the Army of the Potomac. Hooker rejuvenated and refitted the army and in late April began an offensive. On May 1 the armies faced each other in the tangled area near Chancellorsville. Lee, opposing a force numerically far superior, boldly split his army and sent Jackson against Hooker's unprotected left flank. The result has been called Lee's most brilliant victory. The price for Lee was high, however, for among the casualties was "Stonewall" Jackson, mistakenly shot by his own troops.

62. THE WAR COMES TO THE NORTH

Single-page telegram (received copy) from Darius N. Couch to George G. Meade, June 30, 1863. From the Robert Todd Lincoln Collection. MSS

At a meeting in Richmond, General Lee and President Davis agreed that the best way of coping with the mounting problems of the Confederacy—the danger to Vicksburg and alarming shortages, especially of food, in the army—was another invasion of the North. Such a move might also bring foreign recognition and increase the war-weariness of the Union. In June Lee moved his columns into the Shenandoah Valley and turned northward. By the end of the month he was in Pennsylvania, a very real threat to Northern cities. Hasty, and amateurish, defensive preparations were made and the local militia organization called up. In the telegram Darius N. Couch, commanding the militia, reports the location of Confederate forces to Gen. George G. Meade, recently appointed to the command of the Army of the Potomac.

63. GETTYSBURG

(1) "Gettysburg Battlefield." Colored lithograph by Endicott & Co., New York, 1863, after John B. Bachelder; (2) "Battle of Gettysburg, Pa., July 2nd and 3rd, 1863." Lithograph by J. H. Bufford, Boston, 1864. (*See illustration.*) P

On the morning of July 1, a Confederate division under Henry Heth, looking principally for shoes, encountered Federal cavalry under John Buford near the college town of Gettysburg, a place of little military value. A sharp engagement followed, and, as both sides committed more men, it developed into the climactic battle of the war. For 3 days the epic struggle raged, and when it had ended, such names as Culp's Hill, Little Round Top, Devil's Den, and the Angle were a part of our national history. The cost of this supreme effort was nearly 50,000 men. The immediate result was the slow withdrawal of Lee's army toward the Potomac and the end of the last serious threat to the North. A "bird's-eye view" map of Union and Confederate positions and a lithographic battle scene are exhibited.

64. "HIGH TIDE OF THE CONFEDERACY"

"Forming for Pickett's Charge." Pencil drawing by Charles W. Reed. From the Reed Collection.   MSS

The peak of the war was reached on the afternoon of July 3. Federal troops on Cemetery Ridge saw, less than a mile away, Confederate forces massing for a great frontal assault. Led by Virginians and North Carolinians massed by George E. Pickett, 15,000 men in a display of great gallantry tried to break the center of the Union lines. The objective, "a little clump of trees," was reached; but Federal reinforcements arrived, the line held, and the Confederates withdrew under heavy fire, having lost nearly 6,000 men. Soldier-artist Charles W. Reed, of the 9th Massachusetts Battery, depicts Pickett's men preparing to advance.

65. MILITARY LEADERS OF THE UNION

Untitled lithograph by J. D. De Laney, 1865. (*See illustration.*)   P

The approach of Union victory in the closing years of the war coincided with the rise of the four generals shown in this lithograph: Ulysses S. Grant, William Tecumseh Sherman, George H. Thomas, and Philip H. Sheridan.

66. GRANT SPLITS THE CONFEDERACY AT VICKSBURG

"The Siege of Vicksburg." Lithograph by Middleton, Strobridge & Co., Cincinnati, 1863, after A. E. Mathews, 31st. O.V.I. (*See illustration.*)   P

After the surrender of New Orleans (*see* entries 88 and 98), Vicksburg, on a high bluff overlooking the Mississippi River, was strongly fortified by the Confederacy. In November 1862, Grant began a campaign against this great obstacle to Federal control of the river. Failing to reach the city from the north, Grant moved down the west bank, crossed the river, and approached it from the east. Repulsed in attempts to take the city by assault, Grant laid siege to it. After 47 days of heavy bombardment from both the land and gunboats on the river, and with his garrison and the civilian population facing starvation, J. C. Pemberton, commanding the Confederate forces, surrendered on July 4, 1863. Nearly 30,000 men were paroled as prisoners of war. Of these Grant wrote: "They were rationed about as our own men, and from our supplies. The men of the two armies fraternized as if they had been fighting for the same cause. When they passed out of the works they had so long and so gallantly defended . . . not a cheer went up, not a remark was made that would give them pain. I believe there was a feeling of sadness among the Union soldiers at seeing the dejection of their late antagonists." Port Hudson, 300 miles downstream, surrendered 5 days later, and now, as President Lincoln wrote, the Mississippi "flows unvexed to the sea."

67. AN ATTACK UPON UNION SUPPLY LINES IN TENNESSEE

"The War in America: Confederate Sharpshooters Firing on a Federal Supply-Train on the Tennessee River." Photocopy of a wood engraving in *The Illustrated London News*, Dec. 5, 1863, after Frank Vizetelly. (*See illustration.*)   P

At Chickamauga, in September 1863, Braxton Bragg drove William S. Rosecrans' Federal army back to Chattanooga. The Confederates then sought to disrupt its communications and break up its supply trains. Food ran dangerously short as the long "cracker line" was constantly interrupted by Rebel forays such as depicted here by combat artist Vizetelly, who tells us that he himself accompanied this "small force of picked men from General Longstreet's corps, armed with Whitworth telescopic rifles." The detail posted itself "among the crags of Raccoon Mountain, overlooking a road on the other side of the Tennessee River, in use by the Federals. The position chosen was 12 miles in rear of the enemy's works, and, unfortunately for them, was not guarded." Confederate marksmanship in this attack upon a Union wagon train resulted in a road "choked with dead and dying men and mules, and overturned wagons." The infantry escort, "after firing a few shots in return, fled panic-striken, followed by the exulting shouts of the Confederate riflemen."

68. "THE BATTLE OF THE CLOUDS"

"Storming and Capture of Lookout Mountain, November 24, 1863." Colored lithograph by Middleton, Strobridge & Co., Cincinnati. (*See illustration.*)   P

On November 24, 1863, the first step in raising the siege of Chattanooga was taken when forces under Joseph E. Hooker carried the weakened Confederate positions on Lookout Mountain. One of the most dramatic battles of the war, it was hidden from observers below by low hanging clouds and became popularly known as "the battle of the clouds." The next day, a spectacular charge by men under George H. Thomas captured Missionary Ridge and the way to Georgia was opened.

69. CARNAGE IN THE WILDERNESS

"General Wadsworth's Division in Action in the Wilderness, Near the Spot Where the General was Killed." Drawing in pencil and Chinese white by Alfred R. Waud.   P

To offset partially a two-to-one numerical superiority, Lee allowed Grant to cross the Rapidan River and set the stage for the Battle of the Wilderness, May 5–7, 1864. Here, near the old battlefield of Chancellorsville, was fought the most nightmarish battle of the war. Tangled underbrush and trees made vision difficult and cavalry and artillery useless; and when the brush caught fire,

many wounded were trapped in the flames. An aging, anonymous Texas private described the confused fighting: "You Yanks don't call this a battle, do you? At Chickamauga there was at least a rear, but here there ain't neither front nor rear. It's all a * * * mess! And our two armies ain't nothin' but a howlin' mob!" Waud's drawing of the division of James S. Wadsworth, who was mortally wounded in the battle, was reproduced as a wood engraving in *Harper's Weekly*, June 4, 1864.

70. THE ACTION CONTINUES AT SPOTSYLVANIA

Single-page holograph letter from Ulysses S. Grant to Edwin M. Stanton, May 11, 1864. (*See illustration.*) From Grant Miscellany.   MSS

Moving to their left along parallel lines, the armies met again at Spotsylvania Court House, southwest of Fredericksburg. Here, beginning on May 8, in a prolonged and bitter struggle, which included a daylong hand-to-hand fight at the "Bloody Angle," Grant lost 17,000 men, Lee 8,000. Here, too, Grant composed a characteristic letter. Written at 8 a.m. the morning of the 11th and directed to the Secretary of War, it expressed Grant's determination to carry on the campaign in spite of losses and few successes, closing with the words: "I propose to fight it out on this line if it takes all summer." Later the same morning Grant repeated these now famous, oft-quoted words in a fuller communication to Chief of Staff Henry W. Halleck.

71. A "COUNCIL OF WAR" PRIOR TO DISASTER AT COLD HARBOR

Photograph by Timothy H. O'Sullivan, May 21, 1864.   P

Failing to destroy Lee at Spotsylvania, Grant continued "side-slipping toward Richmond" and again moved southeast, the next great engagement of the armies taking place at

Cold Harbor. Here on June 3, 60,000 massed Union soldiers moved against strongly fortified Confederate lines in a direct assault. The result was utter failure, with 5,600 casualties, eliciting the comment from a Confederate colonel that "The dead covered more than five acres of ground about as thickly as they could be laid." O'Sullivan's photograph of Grant and staff officers, taken some days earlier at Grant's temporary headquarters at Massaponax Church, Va, shows the General leaning over a bench to examine a map held by Gen. Meade.

72. THE SIEGE OF PETERSBURG

"Scene of the Explosion, Saturday, July 30th." Drawing in pencil and Chinese white by Alfred R. Waud. P

After the debacle at Cold Harbor, Grant moved his army across the James River and began the prolonged (10-month) siege of Petersburg, the key to Richmond. Constantly pushing his lines westward, he forced Lee to extend his own lines until they were dangerously thin. Decimated by casualties, disease, and desertions, weakened by hunger, the battered and gallant Army of Northern Virginia by the spring of 1865 was near its breaking-point.

Early in the siege of Petersburg, Grant consented to a plan to blow a hole in the Confederate defenses at the point known as Elliott's Salient. Over a period of a month, a 500-foot tunnel was dug to a location under the Confederate battery in the salient, and two short lateral tunnels extended under the enemy trenches. The mine was charged with 8,000 pounds of gunpowder. The explosion which took place the morning of July 30 left a crater 170 feet long and 30 feet deep, into which Federal troops poured, only to be cut down by massed artillery and rifle fire. "The Battle of the Crater," as it has been called, was, in Grant's words, "a stupendous failure."

Waud's drawing, which was reproduced as a wood engraving in *Harper's Weekly*, Aug. 27, 1864, shows Union troops advanc-

ing to and beyond their own entrenchments to the "crater," marked in the middle distance by mounds of earth thrown up by the explosion.

73. SHERIDAN IN THE SHENANDOAH

"Sheridan's Army Following Early Up the Valley of the Shenandoah." Pencil drawing by Alfred R. Waud. (*See illustration.*) P

In the summer of 1864, Lee hoped to relieve some of the pressure on Richmond and forestall a movement to cut off his supplies by sending Jubal A. Early into the Shenandoah Valley. Early defeated Union forces, came down the Shenandoah, crossed the Potomac, and began a march on Washington, levying money and supplies as he moved. On July 11 and 12 he was at the outskirts of the Federal capital, strongly fortified but defended largely by clerks, recruits, and convalescents. After threatening Washington, Early returned to the Shenandoah Valley, destroying supplies and conducting raids into Maryland and burning Chambersburg, Pa. To meet the growing menace, Grant consolidated the forces in the valley under Philip H. Sheridan. With a considerable superiority in numbers, Sheridan gained victories at Winchester and Fisher's Hill. His dramatic ride at Cedar Creek turned apparent defeat into another success over the reinforced Early. With the valley securely in Union hands, Sheridan turned to completely cutting off Lee's food supply by a systematic devastation of the rich agricultural area. Grant's policy was that "crows flying over it . . . will have to carry their provender with them." This drawing of Sheridan's forces in the Valley, in September 1864, was reproduced as a wood engraving in *Harper's Weekly*, Oct. 22, 1864.

74. SHERMAN REACHES THE SEA

"Sherman at Savannah, Ga." Lithograph by the Major & Knapp Eng., Mfg. & Lith. Co., New York, 1865, after Br't Lt. Col. Otto Boetticher. P

In December 1863, President Davis assigned Joseph E. Johnston to the command of the Army of Tennessee. Against this force William T. Sherman and the Federal army advanced in May 1864. In July, by a series of flanking maneuvers, interrupted by an assault and defeat at Kenesaw Mountain, Sherman reached the defenses of Atlanta. The city surrendered on September 1. John B. Hood, commanding the Confederate forces in place of Johnston, withdrew to the southwest. Sherman followed and then returned to pursue a course of action which he described as "a general plan, which amounted substantially to the destruction of Atlanta and the railroad back to Chattanooga, and sallying forth from Atlanta through the heart of Georgia, to capture one or more of the great Atlantic seaports." On November 16, with 60,000 men, Sherman left a burning Atlanta; living off the country, the force reached its destination, Savannah, on December 20.

75. SHERMAN'S PHILOSOPHY OF WAR

Four-page holograph letter from William T. Sherman to Mrs. Caroline Carson, January 20, 1865. From the James L. Petigru Papers. MSS

"War," Sherman commented, "is barbarism at best." On another occasion he cursed all abolitionists but announced his determination to "slay millions," if need be, to preserve the Union. Now, following his "March to the Sea," detested and feared throughout the Confederacy, he explained his philosophy of war in this letter to a Southern friend:

I am making Grand War when lesser objects must be left to follow Greater Results, but I assure you that my study is to accomplish Reason and honor at as small a cost to life and prosperity as possible. I know this end will be attained but how & when are still in the future . . . I thank you for the expression of confidence in me and repeat that you do me but justice in thinking that I am not the scourge and monster that the Southern Press represents me but that I will take infinitely more delight in curing the wounds made by war than in inflicting them.

76. THE LAST MAJOR BATTLE OF THE WAR

Single-page holograph draft of a letter from Abraham Lincoln to Edwin M. Stanton, April 1, 1865. From the Robert Todd Lincoln Collection. MSS

Union victory at Five Forks on April 1, 1865, made the Confederate evacuation of Petersburg and Richmond inevitable. The struggle began on March 31, when Sheridan was driven back upon Dinwiddie Court House. The next day he successfully attacked forces led by George E. Pickett and Fitzhugh Lee. Not far away, at City Point, President Lincoln was following the action, and sent this letter to his Secretary of War, observing: "Sheridan also had pretty hot work yesterday."

77. THE FALL OF PETERSBURG

Photograph by unidentified photographer, April 1865. P

The long siege of Petersburg ended on April 2 as Grant attacked the fortifications early in the morning. Later that day Fort Gregg and Fort Whitworth, the sole remaining strongpoints, were captured. A final assault was scheduled for the next morning, but during the night Lee and the Army of Northern Virginia left the city and began the desperate flight to the west. Shown is the first Federal wagon train entering Petersburg.

78. HOLOCAUST AT RICHMOND

"The Fall of Richmond, Va., on the Night of April 2d, 1865." Colored lithograph by Currier & Ives, New York, 1865. P

Federal troops entered Richmond on April 3. As the last Confederate forces left the city, stores and supplies were set afire. The flames spread, and a hungry, lawless mob looted the city. One of the first actions of the arriving Union forces was to extinguish the fires and bring order to the prostrate

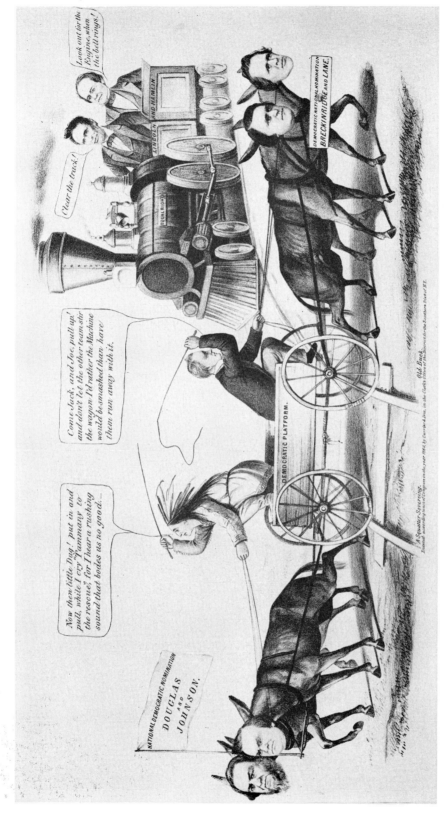

"PROGRESSIVE DEMOCRACY—PROSPECT OF A SMASH UP." *Lithographic cartoon by Currier & Ives, New York, 1860.* (*See entry 3.*)

"THE FIRST FLAG OF INDEPENDENCE RAISED IN THE SOUTH." *Lithograph by R. H. Howell, Savannah, Ga.* *(See entry 4.)*

CHARLESTON

MERCURY

EXTRA:

Passed unanimously at 1.15 o'clock, P. M. December 20th, 1860.

AN ORDINANCE

To dissolve the Union between the State of South Carolina and other States united with her under the compact entitled " The Constitution of the United States of America."

We, the People of the State of South Carolina, in Convention assembled, do declare and ordain, and it is hereby declared and ordained,

That the Ordinance adopted by us in Convention, on the twenty-third day of May, in the year of our Lord one thousand seven hundred and eighty-eight, whereby the Constitution of the United States of America was ratified, and also, all Acts and parts of Acts of the General Assembly of this State, ratifying amendments of the said Constitution, are hereby repealed; and that the union now subsisting between South Carolina and other States, under the name of " The United States of America," is hereby dissolved.

THE

UNION

IS

DISSOLVED!

"CHARLESTON MERCURY EXTRA . . . DECEMBER 20TH, 1860." *Broadside. (See entry 5.)*

"FORT MOULTRIE, CHARLESTON HARBOR." *Watercolor by "A. Vizitelly," 1861. (See entry 8.)*

Arlington 20 April 1861

My dear Cousin Roger—

                    I only
rec.ᵈ to day your letter of the
17ᵗ. Sympathizing with you
in the troubles that are pressing
So heavily upon our beloved
Country, & entirely agreeing
with you in your notions of
allegiance &c, I have been
unable to make up my mind
to raise my hand against my
native State, my relatives, my
children & my home &. I
have therefore resigned my
Commission in the Army &
never desire again to draw my
Sword Save in defence of my
State. I Consider it useless

ROBERT E. LEE MAKES A CHOICE. *First page of holograph letter from Lee to Lt. Roger Jones, April 20, 1861. (See entry 11.)*

TO ARMS!

RALLY FOR THE RIGHT!

Recruits Wanted

For THREE MONTHS SERVICE, IN

COMPANY A

GRAY RESERVES

CAPT. CHARLES S. SMITH.

ARMORY,

810 MARKET STREET,

UP STAIRS.

A TYPICAL RECRUITING BROADSIDE. *Philadelphia, [May 26, 1862].* (*See entry 14.*)

"MISSISSIPPIANS PASSING IN REVIEW BEFORE GENERAL BEAUREGARD AND STAFF." *Wood engraving in* The Illustrated London News, *December 14, 1861.* (*See entry 16.*)

"COMMISSARY DEPARTMENT. ENCAMPMENT OF THE MASS. 6TH REGIMENT OF VOLUNTEERS AT THE RELAY HOUSE NEAR BALTIMORE, MD., 1861." *Lithograph by J. H. Bufford, Boston, 1861.* (See entry 18.)

"ROASTING CORN" AND "FORAGING." *Pencil drawings, probably by Arthur Lumley.* (*See entry* 22.)

HAY FOOT! STRAW FOOT! Photograph by Mathew B. Brady or assistant, 1862. (See entry 28.)

"REV. L. F. DRAKE, CHAPLAIN 31ST OHIO VOLUNTEERS, PREACHING AT CAMP DICK ROBINSON, KY." *Lithograph by Middleton, Strobridge & Co., Cincinnati. (See entry 36.)*

"LEE AND HIS GENERALS." *Lithograph by Tholey, published by John Smith, Philadelphia, 1867.* (*See entry 49.*)

"BATTLE OF GETTYSBURG, PA., JULY 2ND AND 3RD, 1863." *Lithograph by J. H. Bufford, Boston, 1864.* *(See entry 63.)*

MILITARY LEADERS OF THE UNION. *Lithograph by J. D. De Laney, 1865.* (*See entry 65.*)

"THE SIEGE OF VICKSBURG." *Lithograph by Middleton, Strobridge & Co., Cincinnati, 1863. (See entry 66.)*

"CONFEDERATE SHARPSHOOTERS FIRING ON A FEDERAL SUPPLY-TRAIN ON THE TENNESSEE RIVER." *Wood engraving in* The Illustrated London News, *Dec. 5, 1863.* (*See entry 67.*)

city. The Currier and Ives print depicts the conflagration at Richmond.

79. LEE SURRENDERS AT APPOMATTOX

"The Room in the McLean House, at Appomattox C.H., in which Gen. Lee Surrendered to Gen. Grant." Lithograph by Major & Knapp, New York, 1867.   P

In his retreat from Petersburg, Lee had hoped to join with Joseph E. Johnston to make a final stand in North Carolina. Supply depots along the route were destroyed by Federal cavalry racing to cut off his retreat, and an English correspondent wrote: "The sufferings of the men from the pangs of hunger have not been approached in the military annals of the last fifty years." The inevitable end came on April 9 at Appomattox Court House, as effective Confederate resistance ceased, and Lee, in the historic meeting at the McLean House, surrendered to Grant the last proud remnants of the Army of Northern Virginia.

80. SYMBOL OF WAR'S END

Photograph by Timothy H. O'Sullivan, April 1865. (*See illustration.*)   P

View of Union soldiers and stacked arms at Appomattox Court House.

81. LEE'S FAREWELL TO HIS TROOPS

"General Lee's Farewell Address to the Army of Northern Virginia." [Petersburg, Va., 1865(?)]. Broadside.   R

On the day after the surrender, the "pillar of his state" issued his famous General Order no. 9, this broadside printing of which reads:

Headquarters Army of Northern Virginia,
April 10th, 1865.

After four years of arduous service, marked by unsurpassed courage and fortitude, the Army of Northern Virginia has been compelled to yield to overwhelming numbers and resources. I need not tell the survivors of so many hard-fought battles, who have remained steadfast to the last, that I have consented to this result from no distrust of them; but, feeling that valor and devotion could accomplish nothing that could compensate for the loss that would have attended the continuation of the contest, I have determined to avoid the useless sacrifice of those whose past services have endeared them to their countrymen. By the terms of the agreement, officers and men can return to their homes, and remain there until exchanged.

You will take with you the satisfaction that proceeds from the consciousness of duty faithfully performed; and I earnestly pray that a merciful God will extend to you His blessing and protection. With an unceasing admiration of your constancy and devotion to your country, and a grateful remembrance of your kind and generous consideration of myself, I bid you all an affectionate farewell.

R. E. Lee, General.

THE WAR ON THE WATER

The naval war had three dimensions: the blockade of the Southern coastline; the war on the high seas, involving Confederate cruisers which raided Union shipping; and the struggle on the inland waters for the control of the rivers of the Confederacy, principally in the West. The Union navy, supported by the industrial capacity of the North, increased in size from fewer than 100 vessels, largely outmoded in early 1861, to more than 600 by the end of the war. The Confederate navy, non-existent at the beginning of the war, was created by capture, charter, purchase, and foreign contract and was forced to rely on resourcefulness and daring to compensate for the great numerical superiority of the Union fleet and the almost complete lack of shipbuilding facilities in the South.

82. RUNNING THE BLOCKADE

Register of the Arrival and Departure of Vessels at Nassau, Aug. 7, 1861–May 10, 1865. Twenty-page document, with manuscript entries in ink. From the Confederate Miscellany Collection.   MSS

Soon after the outbreak of war President Lincoln proclaimed a blockade of the entire Confederate coastline. The blockade, largely unenforceable at first, increased in effectiveness as the size of the Union fleet grew and did much to create shortages and disrupt the economy of the Confederacy by denying it the advantages of foreign commerce. Much of the naval activity of the Confederacy—including its exploitation of submarines, torpedoes, and ironclad rams—was directed toward breaking the ever-tightening blockade. The most effective countermeasure, however, was that of blockade running by vessels, usually privately owned, which were specially designed to slip by or outrun the Federal warships and, burning smokeless fuel, steam swiftly toward neutral ports. Here the outgoing cargo, generally cotton, was exchanged for European goods, including arms. Blockade running centered on the West Indies. One of the principal ports involved in the activity was Nassau, where the United States consul maintained this record of incoming and outgoing vessels. A typical entry is that of April 6, 1862, noting the arrival of the "British steamer (Blockade runner) *Economist,* from Charleston, where she landed arms" (*see also* entry 83).

83. CONFEDERATE SUPPLIES FROM ENGLAND

"List of Cargo for Confederate Government on Board the *Economist* bound for Nassau." Four-page document, with manuscript entries in ink. (*See illustration.*) From the Pickett Papers.   MSS

The Confederacy supplemented its production of armaments by imports purchased by agents abroad and shipped in foreign vessels. (In the later years of the war the fantastic prices brought by luxury goods in the Southern States attracted blockade runners to non-essential cargoes and led, in 1864, to governmental regulation and licensing of the traffic.) The invoice exhibited, dated January 29, 1862, lists Confederate purchases

made in London and payable in cotton or gold, to be shipped on the British blockade runner *Economist* and including over 10,000 Enfield rifles, 1 million percussion caps, blankets, shoes, and other military equipment.

84. UNION GUNBOATS TAKE FORT HENRY

"Capture of Fort Henry by U.S. Gun Boats Under Command of Flag Officer Foote, February 6th, 1862." Colored lithograph by Middleton, Strobridge & Co., Cincinnati.
P

The nucleus of the Federal fleet on the inland waters was contributed by James B. Eads, a St. Louis engineer, who in less than 100 days constructed eight specially designed, partially armored gunboats. Such vessels as the *Carondelet,* the *St. Louis,* the *Mound City,* and the *Cairo* (the first warship to be sunk by a torpedo) worked closely with land forces in gaining control of the rivers of the West. Early in 1862 a flotilla of seven gunboats left Paducah, Ky.; steamed up the Tennessee River; and on the afternoon of February 6, without assistance from the army, forced the surrender of Fort Henry. Ten days later, on the Cumberland River, gunboats participated in the first major victory for the North, the capture of Fort Donelson (*see* entry 51).

85. APPEARANCE OF THE IRONCLADS

Two-page telegram (received copy) from D. H. Rucker to John A. Dahlgren, March 9, 1862. From the Dahlgren Papers. MSS

On April 20, 1861, Confederate forces occupied the Navy Yard at Norfolk, Va., and found that the steam-frigate *Merrimack* had been only partially destroyed by Federal forces when they withdrew. On the afternoon of March 8, 1862, converted into an ironclad vessel and rechristened the *Virginia,* this warship steamed into Hampton Roads, where a part of the blockading Union fleet lay at anchor. Unaffected by the heavy gunfire dealt her, she rammed and sank the *Cumberland*, left the *Congress* burning, and created great fear in Washington that she could steam unopposed up the Potomac. This telegram, sent "by order of Gen'l. Meigs, Q.M. Gen'l," to Capt. John A. Dahlgren of the United States Navy, concerns a plan to block the channel of the river:

The steamer "Sophis" will leave G Street wharf in ten minutes having in tow eight (8) Canal boats loaded with sufficient stone to sink them, another steamer with eight (8) more will leave in the course of the night . . . the boats are to be sunk if necessary.

86. THE DUEL BETWEEN THE *MONITOR* AND THE *MERRIMACK*

"The First Battle Between 'Iron' Ships of War. The 'Monitor' 2 Guns and 'Merrimac' 10 Guns." Colored lithograph by Henry Bill, 1862. (*See illustration.*) P

Federal authorities were aware that the conversion of the *Merrimack* had begun in June, but it was not until October that construction of the first Union ironclad began. Working from the plans of a Swedish immigrant, John Ericsson, mechanics at the Continental Iron Works at Greenpoint, Brooklyn, labored around the clock until, on January 30, 1862, the *Monitor* was launched. By 9 p.m. on March 8 this "cheesebox on a raft" was anchored in Hampton Roads. The next morning the *Merrimack* again entered the anchorage, making for the *Minnesota*. The *Monitor* came to her defense and there followed the first engagement between ironclad ships of war. At times fighting while almost touching, the two strange vessels did relatively little damage to each other in the indecisive 4-hour struggle, but they established beyond doubt the superiority of armored vessels. Neither craft survived the war. The *Merrimack* was destroyed a few weeks later when the Confederates abandoned Norfolk; the *Monitor* foundered and sank off the North Carolina coast in December 1862.

87. THE CREW OF THE *MONITOR*

Photograph by James F. Gibson. P

Relaxing on the deck of the U.S.S. *Monitor* anchored in the James River, July 9, 1862, is the *Monitor's* crew, some of whom are playing checkers. Visible on the ship's turret are the effects of gunfire from the *Merrimack*.

88. THE UNION NAVY REACHES NEW ORLEANS

"The Battle of New Orleans." Colored lithograph by T. Sinclair, Philadelphia. (*See illustration.*) P

New Orleans was defended by two forts, Jackson and St. Philip, situated on opposite banks some 60 miles down the Mississippi, a chain boom stretching between them. Patrolling the river was a small fleet which included the ram *Manassas* (*see* entry 98); some gunboats; and fire rafts, to be set ablaze and allowed to drift into attacking vessels. On April 18, 1862, David G. Farragut, commanding the West Gulf Blockading Squadron, sent Porter's mortar flotilla to bombard the forts, but with little effect. At 2 a.m. on April 24 he began a movement to run his fleet of wooden vessels by the forts, smash the boom, and steam up the river. He succeeded spectacularly, as depicted, and about 9 a.m. on April 25 was anchored before the defenseless city. Surrender came that afternoon, and on May 1 control of the city was given to Union army forces commanded by the controversial Benjamin F. Butler.

89. THE WAR ON THE HIGH SEAS

"The U.S. Sloop of War 'Kearsarge' 7 Guns, Sinking the Pirate 'Alabama' 8 Guns, off Cherbourg, France, Sunday, June 19th, 1864." Colored lithograph by Currier & Ives, New York. P

While throngs of spectators lined the coast to watch, one of the two great naval duels of the war took place off Cherbourg, France. The *Alabama,* built in England, had put in at Cherbourg for repairs after destroying 58 merchant vessels in her 2-year career. Three days later a Federal warship, the *Kearsarge,* appeared outside the harbor. On Sunday, June 19, 1864, the *Alabama* steamed out, and about seven miles offshore the engagement began. Although the vessels were about equally matched, the *Kearsarge* gun crews were more experienced and better trained, and their superior marksmanship sank the Confederate cruiser in less than 2 hours. The activities of the *Alabama* and other cruisers, such as the *Shenandoah* (which as late as June 1865 was destroying whalers in the Bering Sea, not knowing that the war had ended), had little effect upon the ultimate outcome of the war. The consequences of their actions, however, would last many years. Not until 1872 were the claims for reparations brought by this nation against Great Britain settled; and much time would be necessary before the American merchant marine, depleted both by sinkings and the transfer of vessels to the registries of other nations, would regain the status it had held before the war.

90. VICTORS OVER THE *ALABAMA*

Photograph by unidentified photographer, 1864.   P

Capt. John A. Winslow (third from left) posing with his officers on the deck of the *Kearsarge* after the sinking of the *Alabama.*

91. MINES IN NAVAL WARFARE

"Infernal Machines Discovered in the Potomac Near Aquia Creek by the Flotilla for Whose Destruction They Were Intended." Drawing in pencil and Chinese white by Alfred R. Waud.   P

Mines were used by both sides in the war and were responsible for the sinking of 22 Union and 6 Confederate vessels. In rivers and harbors, allowed to float on the surface or

anchored below it, these "torpedoes," as they were called, were exploded either on contact or electrically. Approaching a floating mine, in the drawing, is a boat from the Potomac flotilla which, during June 1861, was engaged in the bombardment of Confederate batteries at Aquia Creek and Mathias Point, Va. The flotilla included the gunboat *Thomas Freeborn* (commanded by James H. Ward) and the 11-gun sloop *Pawnee,* both of which are depicted. Waud's sketch "from a photograph by James F. Gibson," was reproduced as a wood engraving in the *New York Illustrated News,* July 22, 1861.

92. "DAMN THE TORPEDOES, FULL SPEED AHEAD!"

"The Great Naval Victory in Mobile Bay, August 5th, 1864." Colored lithograph by Currier & Ives, New York.   P

The great disparity in the sizes of the navies was dramatically illustrated at the battle of Mobile Bay. Here the ironclad *Tennessee,* commanded by Franklin Buchanan, the first commandant of Annapolis, opposed almost singlehandedly a Federal fleet of 18 vessels led by David G. Farragut. On August 5, 1864, Farragut's fleet forced a passage into the bay. When one of his monitors was sunk by a torpedo, the old Admiral, lashed to the rigging of his flagship, the *Hartford,* cried, "Damn the torpedoes, full speed ahead" (a phrase which immediately caught the fancy of the Northern public). In the bay, the *Tennessee* damaged three of the Union vessels, but, attacked by the entire fleet, including three monitors, was forced to surrender. With the fall of Fort Morgan, guarding the passage to the bay, on August 23, another Confederate outlet was sealed off.

93. LAST CONFEDERATE PORT CLOSED

"Bombardment of Fort Fisher, Jan. 15th, 1865." Lithograph by Endicott & Co., Boston, 1865, after T. F. Laycock.   P

By the end of 1864, Wilmington, N.C., was

the only major port available to the Confederates. The defense of the city was Fort Fisher on the Cape Fear River, and in December 1864 the Confederate forces gained a victory when an attack on that point by Army and Navy units commanded by Benjamin F. Butler failed utterly. Early in January 1865, another joint effort was made. A large naval force led by David D. Porter bombarded the fort for 3 days. On January 15 troops were landed; at 10 p.m., after bitter resistance, the garrison surrendered.

LITHOGRAPHIC VIEWS OF THE WAR

Many of the scenes in this section and the following ("Lithographic Views of Military Establishments") are based upon drawings that were prepared by eyewitnesses to the scenes depicted. Some were civilian observers, but a large number were servicemen. They include Pvt. Thomas Carr (6th New York Cavalry), Corp. Edward S. Lloyd (Massachusetts 3d Battalion of Rifles), and, among the volunteer infantry regiments, Lt. Nathan B. Abbott (20th Connecticut), Sgt. John L. Richardson (7th Michigan), Pvt. Alfred E. Mathews (31st Ohio), Corp. Joseph M. Thurston (90th Ohio), and Pvt. William C. Schwartzburg (24th Wisconsin).

At least one of these soldier-artists, Alfred E. Mathews, the most prolific of the group, was a trained artist. A 30-year-old itinerant bookseller and artist at the outbreak of the war, he served 3 years with the 31st Ohio Volunteer Infantry and during that time recorded actions in Kentucky and at Corinth, Vicksburg, Stone River, and Chattanooga. He was a skilled observer and his sketches must be regarded as important historical documents. Those of the siege of Vicksburg drew the praises of Grant himself, who told the artist that they were "among the most accurate and true to life I have ever seen. They reflect great credit upon you as a delineator of landscape views." Mathews apparently did not always witness the actions he depicted. It is doubtful, for instance, that he saw any of the fighting at Logan's Cross

Roads or the death of Zollicoffer (*Cf.* entries 94 and 95). This depiction no doubt is based upon an examination of the scene of battle and the testimony of those who were there. Mathews' views, of which he made more than 35 (14 are included in this catalog), were printed by lithographic firms in Cincinnati, chiefly Middleton, Strobridge, and Company.

Other soldier-artists represented in this publication are Br't. Lt. Col. Otto Boetticher (68th New York), Confederate Sgt. Conrad Wise Chapman (59th Virginia), and Pvt. Charles W. Reed (9th Massachusetts Battery). There is in addition one sailor-artist, Thomas F. Laycock, U.S.N.

94. "The Battle of Logan's Cross Roads, Fought on the 19th of January, 1862." Lithograph by Middleton, Strobridge & Co.(?), Cincinnati, after A. E. Mathews, 31st O.V., U.S.A.
P

In the western theatre early in the war, Union forces (the 2d Minnesota, the 4th Kentucky, and the 10th Indiana), commanded by George H. Thomas, moved to prevent a Confederate advance into Kentucky from eastern Tennessee. In the battle of Logan's Cross Roads (or Mill Springs), near Somerset, Ky., the inadequately equipped rebels, led by Maj. Gen. George B. Crittenden and Brig. Gen. Felix K. Zollicoffer (whose death is depicted), were defeated.

95. "Union Forces Crossing Fishing Creek." Lithograph by Middleton, Strobridge & Co., Cincinnati, 1862, after A. E. Mathews, 31st Reg. Ohio Volunteers.
P

Crossing a tributary of the Cumberland are several regiments of Ohio Volunteers (the 17th, 31st, 35th, and 38th), commanded by Gen. Albin Schoepf and marching to the support of Thomas at Logan's Cross Roads, January 19, 1862. (*See* entry 94.) They reportedly arrived after the fighting was over.

96. "The First Union Dress Parade in Nashville." Lithograph by Middleton, Stro-

bridge & Co., Cincinnati, after A. E. Mathews, 31st Regt., O.V., U.S.A.   P

The 51st Regiment of Ohio Volunteers is shown parading on March 4, 1862, in Nashville. The city was abandoned to Union forces after the surrender of Fort Donelson (*see* entry 51).

97. "Battle of Shiloh. The Gunboats Tylor [*sic*] and Lexington Supporting the National Troops, by Firing up the Ravine Back of Pittsburg Landing." Lithograph by Middleton, Strobridge & Co., after A. E. Mathews, 31st Reg't, O.V., U.S.A.   P

On the afternoon of April 6, 1862, Federal forces on the Shiloh battlefield (*see* entry 54), forced back almost to the river at Pittsburg Landing, were reinforced by the cannon fire of the gunboats *Tyler* (10 guns) and *Lexington* (7 guns). These armed vessels were originally side-wheel river steamers. Purchased by the Navy the year before in Cincinnati, they were cut down and surfaced with thick planks to make warships.

98. "Com. Farragut's Fleet, Passing the Forts on the Mississippi, April 24th, 1862." Colored lithograph by Currier & Ives, New York, 1862.   P

Moving up the river, between Fort St. Philip (on the east bank) and Fort Jackson (on the west), are the ships of the New Orleans expedition. (*See* entry 88.) Depicted in the foreground is the U.S. frigate *Mississippi* sinking the rebel ram *Manassas*. In the engagement the Confederacy lost two additional (unfinished) ironclads, the *Louisiana* and the *Mississippi*.

99. "Capture of a Rebel Lunette, near Yorktown, Va., April 26th, 1862." Colored lithograph by Endicott & Co., New York, after John B. Bachelder.   P

An incident which occurred during the Peninsular Campaign and the siege of Yorktown by the Army of the Potomac. Con-

federate earthworks in an advanced position were captured and leveled by detachments from the 1st and 11th Massachusetts volunteers, commanded by Brig. Gen. Cuvier Grover. (*See also* item 53.)

100. "The 31st Reg't Ohio Vol., [Col. M. B. Walker] Building Breastworks and Embrasures Before Corinth, Miss., May 1862." Lithograph by Middleton, Strobridge & Co., Cincinnati, after A. E. Mathews, 31st Regt., O.V., U.S.A.   P

After "Bloody Shiloh" (*see* items 54 and 97), Halleck determined to take Corinth, 20 miles to the southwest in Mississippi. Against a Union army of 110,000 men (Grant's Army of the Tennessee, Buell's Army of the Ohio, and Pope's Army of the Mississippi), Beauregard could bring to bear but 66,000. To save his army, he was forced, after a short siege, to abandon the city.

101. "On the March from Hamburg to Camp Before Corinth." Lithograph by Middleton, Strobridge & Co., Cincinnati, after A. E. Mathews, 31st Reg't., O.V.I.   P

Fording a stream, on April 28, 1862, are troops and supply wagons of the 10th Regiment of Iowa Volunteers, moving from Hamburg Landing, Tenn., to join in the advance upon and siege of Corinth, Miss. (Apr. 29–May 30).

102. "The Charge of the First Maryland Regiment at the Death of Ashby." Lithograph by A. Hoen & Co., Baltimore, 1862(?). (*See illustration.*)   P

On June 6, 1862, a Confederate brigade (including the 58th Virginia and the 1st Maryland), which was covering Jackson's retreat up the Shenandoah, encountered the 13th Pennsylvania Reserves ("Bucktail Rifles") near Harrisonburg, Va. Severe fighting ensued; the "Bucktails" suffered heavy losses, including the capture of their commander, Lt. Col. Thomas L. Kane; and the Confederate leader, Turner Ashby, who had acquired legendary fame for his ability to conduct rear-guard actions, was killed.

103. "Bataille de Gaine's Mill, Virginie (27 Juin 1862)." Lithograph by Lemercier after drawing by François d'Orléans, 1862.   P

The second of the engagements which took place during the retreat of Union forces in the Seven Days' Battle (*see* item 55) occurred at Gaines' Mill, Va. (First Cold Harbor or Chickahominy) on June 27, 1862. In this battle scene Fitz-John Porter, commanding the 5th Corps, is depicted issuing orders to certain of his staff, chiefly foreign officers who at the time were attached to the Army of the Potomac. Foremost of the officers on horseback, left to right, are: Gen. Porter (for his able defense he was brevetted Brigadier General); Capt. Louis Philippe d'Orléans (Comte de Paris), pretender to the throne of France; and his brother, Capt. Robert d'Orléans (Duc de Chartres). When trouble arose between their country and the United States over Mexico, the Orléans princes returned to France. The lithograph, incidentally, is based on a drawing by their uncle François d'Orléans (Prince de Joinville), who was an observer. Other mounted officers depicted are: the mustached Col. Paul von Radowitz, a former officer of the Prussian Garde du Corps, who, in September 1861, joined the staff of the Army of the Potomac, where he served throughout the war; Gen. George W. Morell, commander of the 1st Division of the V Corps (May 18–Oct. 30, 1862); and (extreme right) George G. Meade, who at this time was a brigadier general and who was severely wounded 3 days later in the battle of White Oak Swamp.

104. "General Kearney's Gallant Charge at the Battle of Chantilly, Va., 1st of September 1862." Colored lithograph by Tholey, published by John Smith, Philadelphia, 1867.   P

The day after the victory at 2d Bull Run (Aug. 29–30, 1862), Lee attempted to cut off Federal forces retreating to Washington (via Centreville). In this he was unsuccessful, for Union Maj. Gens. Phil Kearney and Isaac I. Stevens conducted a brilliant rear-guard action at Chantilly (or Ox Hill), Va., in which both lost their lives.

105. "The 21st Reg't Wisconsin Vol., Crossing the Pontoon Bridge, at Cincinnati, Saturday, Sept. 13, 1862." Lithograph by Middleton, Strobridge & Co., Cincinnati, after A. E. Mathews, 31st Reg't., O.V. (*See illustration.*)   P

The 21st Wisconsin Volunteer Infantry was organized at Oshkosh and left the State on September 11, 1862. In 5 days, passing en route through Cincinnati, it marched to encamp at Louisville, Ky. Depicted is Col. Benjamin J. Sweet leading his regiment out of Cincinnati and across the Ohio River.

106. "The Battle of Stone River or Murfreesboro. Charge of Gen. Negley's Division Across Stone River, on Friday, January 2nd, 1863." Lithograph by Middleton, Strobridge & Co., Cincinnati, 1863, after A. E. Mathews, 31st O.V.I.   P

Under the command of Brig. Gen. James S. Negley, the 2d Division of George H. Thomas' XIV Corps, Army of the Cumberland, charges across Stone River to engage Confederate forces under Braxton Bragg. (*See also* entry 60.)

107. "The Army of the Cumberland in Front of Chattanooga." Lithograph by Donaldson & Elmes, Cincinnati, 1863, after A. E. Mathews, 31st Regiment, O.V.I.   P

Almost routed in the battle of Chickamauga on Sept. 19–21, 1863, Rosecrans retreated with his Army of the Cumberland to Chattanooga, where it was besieged (Sept. 24–Nov. 23) by Bragg. The near-disaster cost him his command and on Oct. 20, 1863, subsequent to the sketching of this scene, he **was** replaced by George H. Thomas ("The Rock of Chickamauga"). The lithograph shows the positions and camps of three divisions of Thomas' XIV Corps—the first commanded by Lovell Harrison Rousseau, the second by James S. Negley, and the third by John Milton Brannan. In the far distance is Lookout Mountain; in the foreground, the breastworks and embrasures of "Fort Grose," dominated by "Cockerill's Battery, 1st Ohio."

108. "Gallant Charge of the 6th N.Y. Cavalry, on the 11th Oct. 1863, at Brandy Station, Va." Colored lithograph by Henry C. Eno, New York, 1864, after Thomas Carr, Troop F, 6th N.Y. Cav'y.   P

Skirmishing during the Bristoe campaign (Oct. 9–Nov. 9, 1863), beside the tracks of the Orange and Alexandria R.R., is the 6th New York Cavalry ("Second Ira Harris Guard") under the command of "the intrepid" Maj. William P. Hall. At Brandy Station (or Fleetwood), there took place, earlier in the year (June 9), what has been called the greatest cavalry conflict of the war. Here Alfred Pleasonton's Union troopers, clashing with those of Jeb Stuart, demonstrated for the first time their ability to fight on even terms with the Confederate cavalry. As Henry B. McClellan, who rode with Stuart, expressed it, the battle *"made* the Federal cavalry. Up to that time confessedly inferior to the Southern horsemen, they gained on this day that confidence in themselves and in their commanders which enabled them to contest so fiercely the subsequent battle-fields of June, July, and October."

109. "Battle of Pleasant Hill, Near Shreveport, Red River, La." Colored lithograph by Buffords Print Publishing House, Boston, 1864(?), after [Joseph E.?] Baker.   P

In Louisiana in 1864 Gen. Edmund Kirby-Smith thwarted the Red River expedition of Gen. Nathaniel P. Banks with defeats at Sabine Cross Roads on April 8 and at Pleasant Hill on April 9. Banks' intention had been the invasion of eastern Texas.

110. "The Battle of the Wilderness, Va., May 5th & 6th, 1864." Colored lithograph by Currier & Ives, New York.   P

For a general description of the Wilderness battlefield, *see* entry 69.

111. "View of Public Square, Atlanta, Ga." Colored lithograph by Henry C. Eno, New York, after Lieut. N. B. Abbott, 20th C't.   P

Atlanta was evacuated by the Confederates on September 1, 1864. The next day Henry W. Slocum's 20th Army Corps occupied the city, where it remained for over 2 months. One regiment, the 2d Massachusetts Volunteers (whose commander, Col. William Cogswell, was appointed post-commandant), pitched its tents (depicted) in the park before City Hall. The lithograph also shows, in the foreground, a 20th Corps cavalry detail. For information about the artist, *see* entries 125–126.

LITHOGRAPHIC VIEWS OF MILITARY ESTABLISHMENTS

Included are views of camps (entries 112 to 118), forts and posts (entries 119 to 126), and hospitals and prisons (entries 127 to 132).

112. "Camp Bates, 3d. N.Y. Vol. Cavalry." Lithograph by Sarony, Major & Knapp, New York, 1862(?), after Combe.   P

Early in the war, this cavalry camp on the

upper Potomac near Poolesville, Md., under the command of Col. James H. Van Alen, formed part of the defenses of Washington. "Van Alen's cavalry" saw action in Virginia, from October 1861 to April 1862, at Goose Creek, Edwards Ferry, Winchester, and in the Shenandoah. It served thereafter in the Department of North Carolina.

113. "Camp Benton. 7th Regt. Michigan Volunteers. Col. J. R. Grosvenor. Situated Near Edwards Ferry." Colored lithograph by A. Hoen & Co., Baltimore, 1862, after Sergt. J. L. Richardson. P

Another outpost on the upper Potomac, early in the war, was the camp of the 7th Michigan Volunteer Infantry. Under the command of Col. Ira R. Grosvenor, this regiment left the State in September 1861 and encamped for the winter in Virginia, near Edwards Ferry. The following spring it joined the Army of the Potomac in the Peninsula. Under the command of Col. Norman J. Hall (from July 1862), it distinguished itself in many battles, especially at Fredericksburg where, against murderous fire from the opposite shore, it volunteered to cross the Rappahannock in pontoon boats. The lithograph is based upon a drawing by John L. Richardson who, at the age of 27, enlisted as first sergeant in Company E; on April 15, 1862, he was commissioned first lieutenant.

114. "View of Camp Dennison." Colored lithograph by Middleton, Strobridge & Co., Cincinnati, 1865. P

One of the leading mobilization and training centers in Ohio, Camp Dennison was located, amid rolling hills, 16 miles to the northeast of Cincinnati. Established in the spring of 1861, when William Dennison was Governor of the State, the camp later in the war was used also as a general hospital and was garrisoned by a Veteran Reserve Corps; it was closed in September 1865. In this lithographic view, which looks to the north, is shown the camp, situated on the Little Miami River (far right) and bisected by the Little Miami Railroad. On the left is a row of hospital barracks; at the upper right, above the "village," are cavalry quarters.

115. "Camp Oliver, 25th. Mass. V. Infantry, New Berne, N.C., 1862–3." Colored lithograph by Sarony, Major & Knapp, New York, after Combe. P

Established near New Bern after the capture of that city by Federal forces on March 14, 1862, Camp Oliver was the base of operations throughout the war for the 25th Massachusetts Volunteer Infantry. Attached to Burnside's Expeditionary Corps, the 25th had previously (Feb. 8) taken part in the capture and occupation of Roanoke Island, which gave the Union control of Albemarle Sound. Thereafter it was largely occupied with guard, picket, and outpost duty but participated during the summer of 1864 in the battle of Cold Harbor and the siege of Petersburg.

116. "Camp of the Duryea's Zuaves, Federal Hill, Baltimore, Md." Colored lithograph by E. Sachse & Co., Baltimore, 1861. P

The colorful 5th New York Volunteer Infantry, commonly known as "Duryea's Zouaves," was but one of a number of regiments, Union and Confederate, that adopted the uniforms of the original Zouaves of the French colonial service. This particular organization was famous not alone for its dress but for the precision of its drill and its courage in combat. While the "zoo-zoos" were stationed in Baltimore (July 26, 1861– April 11, 1862), thousands reportedly turned out of an evening to watch them parade. These well-disciplined troops fought with the Army of the Potomac in the Peninsular Campaign, in the Seven Days' Retreat (distinguishing themselves especially at Gaines' Mill), and in the battles of 2d Bull Run, Antietam, Fredericksburg, and Chancellorsville.

117. "Camp of the Massachusetts Second Comp'y, Light Artillery, at Stewarts Place, Baltimore, Md." Colored lithograph by E. Sachse & Co., Baltimore, 1861.   P

This is Camp Hale on the Baltimore estate of Confederate Gen. George H. ("Maryland") Steuart, where, from August 1861 to February 1862, the Second Massachusetts Light Artillery, or Nim's Battery as it was generally called, was stationed prior to service in the Departments of the Mississippi and the Gulf. Ormand F. Nim's Company, according to newspaper accounts of the period, numbered about 150 men and included 140 horses, 21 gun carriages, 4 baggage wagons, an ambulance, and 6 cannon which had been manufactured at the famed Watervliet Arsenal, Troy, N.Y., and rifled at Alger's Foundry in South Boston (*see also* entry 190). In February 1862 Nim's Battery went into camp at Old Point Comfort, remaining there until April 1863, when it embarked with Gen. Butler's expedition against New Orleans.

118. "Camp of Massachusetts Sixth Regt. Vols., Suffolk, Va." Colored lithograph by J. H. Bufford, Boston, 1863.   P

This camp at Suffolk, Va., was "home" for the "Old Sixth" from September 1862 until May 1863. During this period it served with the 7th Army Corps, Department of Virginia, in expeditions to Blackwater, Beaver Dam Church, and Yuni, and at the Siege of Suffolk (April 12–May 4, 1863). The famous regiment was one of the first units to respond in the spring of 1861 to Lincoln's call for 3-month troops to defend Washington (*see* entry 15); now, under Col. Albert S. Follansbee (who the year before had been Captain of Co. C), it was responding to a call for 9-month volunteers. The lithograph is said to be "from an original drawing in possession of" Follansbee.

119. "Fort Albany, at Arlington Heights. Erected 1861 by the 25th Regiment, N.Y.S.M." Colored lithograph by Murray & Co., 1862. (*See illustration.*)   P

One of several fortifications on the Virginia side of the Potomac, erected early in 1861 for the defense of Washington, Fort Albany was situated near the intersection of Columbia Turnpike and the old Alexandria & Georgetown Road. Under the command of Col. Michael K. Bryan, this earthwork, with its bastions, parapets, and gun embrasures, was constructed between May and July by the 3-month volunteer troops of the 25th New York Regiment.

Washington was pitifully weak in defenses at the start of the conflict; by war's end, however, a system of 68 enclosed forts and batteries in Virginia, Maryland, and the District protected the Federal city.

120. "Fort McHenry, Baltimore, Md., 1861. Occupied by the 3rd Battalion of Rifles, M.V.M." Colored lithography by J. H. Bufford, Boston, 1862, after Corporal E. S. Lloyd.   P

On May 2, 1861, Fort McHenry was garrisoned by the Massachusetts Third Battalion of Rifles, under the command of Maj. Charles Devins, Jr. Nothing of significance occurred during the battalion's tour of duty, and it was mustered out on August 3. Corp. E. S. Lloyd of "Dodds carvers," the soldier-artist who sketched this scene, was a member of Co. D, led by Capt. Albert Dodd.

121. "Fort Mitchell." Lithograph by Middleton, Strobridge & Co., Cincinnati, after A. E. Mathews, 31st Reg't. Ohio Volunteers.   P

A view of Fort Mitchell, mounting four cannon, as it looked when the newly organized 104th O.V.I. was on picket duty in defense of Cincinnati against a threatened attack by Kirby-Smith. Severe skirmishing took place within sight of the fort on September 10, 1862. Situated 4 miles southwest of Covington, Ky., the earthworks were named after Gen. Ormsby M. Mitchel, who briefly in the fall of 1861 commanded the Department of the Ohio, with headquarters at Cincinnati.

122. "Fortress Monroe, Old Point Comfort, & Hygeia Hotel, Va., in 1861 & 1862. The Key to the South." Colored lithograph by E. Sachse & Co., Baltimore, 1862.   P

Located at Old Point Comfort on the tip of the peninsula formed by the York and the James rivers, Fortress Monroe commanded Hampton Roads, Va., and, during the Peninsular Campaign, as "the key to the South," served as a base for McClellan's superbly trained Army of the Potomac. (*See also* entries 53 and 55.)

The historic moated fortification was begun in 1819. By the time of the Civil War its construction costs, according to the *Hand-Book for the War* (Boston, 1861), had already amounted to $2½ million. The Hygeia Hotel, a fashionable resort at its base, was "extemporized" in 1862 as a hospital for Union sick and wounded.

123. "Fort Sumter, Charleston Harbor, S.C." Colored lithograph by Currier & Ives, New York.   P

An artist's conception of Fort Sumter as it was prior to its bombardment and capture by the Confederates under Beauregard (*see* entry 9). Pentagonal in shape and of brick construction, the fort was about 350 by 300 feet in size, with walls 40 feet high and up to 12 feet thick. Although begun in 1829, the fort in 1861 was as yet incomplete. It had an intended capacity of 140 guns, but fewer than half that number were actually fired in defense of the fort.

124. "Fort Sumter, December 9th, 1863, View from South West Angle." Lithograph by J. Bien, New York, 1865(?). (*See illustration.*)   P

Shattered walls and a gutted interior are all that remained of Fort Sumter after a week's bombardment by the Union Navy during August 1863. Infantry, replacing the fort's artillery, repulsed an attempt to land Union forces, and Fort Sumter (and Charleston) remained in Confederate hands almost until the end of the war. The lithograph is said to be based on a photocopy of an ink drawing procured soon after the close of the war from Lieut. Col. Stephen Elliott, in command of Confederate artillery during the siege.

125. "Military Post, Anderson, Tenn." Colored lithograph by Henry C. Eno, New York, 1864(?), after N. B. Abbott.   P

Soldiers' barracks and other buildings of a Federal military post in south central Tennessee, near the Alabama border, about 30 miles southwest of Chattanooga. In the foreground, a train of the United States Military Rail Road approaches the station at Anderson.

Sgt. Nathan B. Abbott, who drew this sketch, was a member of Company H of the 20th Connecticut Volunteer Infantry. In the fall of 1863 this regiment was transferred from the Army of the Potomac to the Army of the Cumberland. Sent to help protect Federal lines of communication between Chattanooga and Nashville, it arrived at Stephenson, Ala., just south of the Tennessee border, early in October, and was assigned to guard duty along the Nashville and Chattanooga Rail Road.

126. "View of Military Post, Tracy City, Tenn." Hand-colored lithograph by Henry C. Eno, New York, after Lieut. N. B. Abbott.   P

Stockades, barracks, and other buildings of a Federal military post in south central Tennessee, about 30 miles northwest of Chattanooga.

Soldier-artist Abbott was commissioned second lieutenant on March 22, 1864. His drawing, therefore, must have been made some time after that date but before May, when the 20th Connecticut left to serve with Sherman in the advance to Atlanta (*see also* entry 111).

127. "Mount Pleasant Hospitals, Washington, D.C." Colored lithograph by Charles Magnus, New York, 1862.   P

This 10-ward hospital was one of the first of a number of "pavilion hospitals" constructed by the Federal Government, after considerable urging from the U.S. Sanitary Commission. (*See also* entry 140). It was completed in April 1862. As the lithograph shows, provisions was made for an additional 1,026 patients by the erection of 57 tent-pavilions, each consisting of three hospital tents placed together, arranged in parallel rows with intervening avenues.

128. "Camp Douglas, Chicago, Illinois, 1864." Colored lithograph by Charles Shober, Chicago.   P

This 60-acre prison camp and hospital, originally established in 1861 as a training camp for Illinois volunteers, was located on Chicago's Cottage Grove Avenue, slightly south of the city's suburbs. In 1864, according to the lithograph, the camp was garrisoned by a Veteran Reserve Corps of "1800" and held "6,000" prisoners. There is evidence, however, that at one time or another during the year the strength of the garrison was less and the number of prisoners considerably more. Camp Douglas was one of the camps which in 1864 figured in an unsuccessful plot by Copperheads to free Confederate prisoners, arm them, and stage an uprising throughout the West.

129. "Libby Prison, Richmond, Va." Colored lithograph by E. Sachse & Co., 1864, after W. C. Schwartzburg, Co. A, 24th Wisc. Vols.   P

Union officers only were confined in this three-storied Confederate prison which, before the war, was a warehouse belonging to the Richmond firm of Libby & Sons, shipchandlers and grocers.

In February 1864, 109 prisoners made their escape from Libby through a tunnel dug under the street, over half of them reaching safety behind Union lines. A little later, after a series of Federal cavalry raids, which the Confederates feared were aimed at the freeing of prisoners in Richmond, the inmates were moved south, to Macon, Ga. (and at the same time, enlisted men, who were confined on nearby Belle Isle in the James River, were transferred to Andersonville).

Pvt. William C. Schwartzburg of the 24th Wisconsin Volunteers, who drew this sketch, was wounded and taken prisoner at Chickamauga. As an enlisted man he would probably have been imprisoned at nearby Belle Isle; or, possibly, being wounded, confined in a hospital perhaps within sight of Libby. Regimental histories record that he was mustered out (June 10, 1865); he therefore either escaped, or, more likely, was exchanged.

130. "U.S.A. Genl. Hospital, Little Rock, Arkansas." Colored lithograph by A. Trochsler, Boston, 1864. (*See illustration.*)   P

Throughout the war, especially in the west, military hospitals were often improvised from existing structures, such as hotels, factories, warehouses, and school buildings. In Little Rock, St. John's College (a military academy) was converted into a Confederate hospital, which, after the capture of the city by Union forces in September 1863, was continued as a United States establishment. Reopened after the war, the college, situated in the southeast section of the city, closed its doors about a decade thereafter. This historic red-brick building with its twin crenelated towers was destroyed by fire on January 18, 1890.

131. "View of Danville, Va., where Union Prisoners are Confined." Colored lithograph by Endicott & Co., New York, 1865, after J. M. Thurston, Company F, 90th Ohio Infantry.   P

At Danville, Va., more than 2,000 Federal prisoners were confined, during late 1864, in the two- and three-storied tobacco factories depicted. Officers were held in "prison no. 3," the large brick three-storied building facing Spring Street (center of view), immediately north of Union Street. Behind this building were prisons 1, 2, and (across Spring Street) 4; in these the enlisted men were confined.

132. "View of Rebel Hospitals, Danville, Va., Where Sick Union Prisoners are Kept." Colored lithograph by Endicott & Co., New York, 1865, after J. M. Thurston, Company F, 90th Ohio Vols.   P

Corp. Joseph M. Thurston, who sketched this and the preceding view, enlisted on July 23, 1862, at the age of 21, in the 90th Ohio Volunteer Infantry. On September 20, 1863, he was captured at Chickamauga. Following his imprisonment at Danville and his exchange, he was mustered out of service on June 26, 1865.

CARE OF THE SICK AND THE WOUNDED

The war, when it came, found the medical departments of both the Union and the Confederate armies to a great extent unprepared. Their doctors were few and largely untrained in military medicine and surgery. Moreover, a long war was not foreseen, and many of the hospitals of the first year were improvisations. Only gradually, beginning in 1862, were they replaced by hospitals of a radical new design, based on the one-story pavilion.

Before the end of the conflict, Northern and Southern doctors were to treat hundreds of thou-

sands of casualties from wounds, and cases of sickness running into the millions. Fortunately the staggering burden was not borne alone; relief agencies, local and nationwide in scope, lent assistance. Chief of these in the North was the United States Sanitary Commission, which, with the sanction of the War Department, performed duties comparable to those of the American Red Cross in later wars. In the South, State associations, supported by public and private funds, provided similar services.

As in all wars prior to World War I, more men died of disease than from battle. It is estimated that of 500,000 or more soldiers who succumbed, at least two of every three died, not of wounds, but from sickness. It has been observed, however, that, as compared with previous wars of the 19th century, the Civil War was a relatively healthy one. The decreased degree of mortality can to a great extent be ascribed to improved methods of sanitation and hygiene.

133. GUIDE FOR CONFEDERATE SURGEONS

Chisolm, Julian J. *A Manual of Military Surgery, for the Use of Surgeons in the Confederate Army; with an Appendix of the Rules and Regulations of the Medical Department of the Confederate Army.* Richmond, Va., 1861.   R

At the outbreak of war many medical officers, Union and Confederate, had had little, if any, experience in military surgery. The South, moreover, lacked the technical works with which to instruct its doctors in the subject. The first Confederate publication to meet the need was this treatise by Dr. Julian J. Chisolm, professor of surgery at the Medical College of South Carolina, who is said to have been the first Confederate commissioned as a medical officer. Chisolm's work, which underwent several revisions after its original publication in 1861, became standard and was widely circulated, together with manuals by other Confederate medical officers, notably *An Epitome of Practical Surgery, for Field and Hospital* (Richmond, 1863), by

Edward Warren and *A Manual of Military Surgery, Prepared for the Use of the Confederate States Army* (Richmond, 1863), prepared by a group of officers "by order of Surgeon General," Samuel P. Moore.

134. AMBULANCES OF THE CIVIL WAR

Photograph by unidentified photographer, May 2, 1864.   P

In this view of the Ambulance Corps of the 57th New York Infantry removing wounded from Marye's Heights battlefield, are to be seen the two basic types of ambulances (four-wheeled and two-wheeled) made use of during the war. The Federals allotted one four-wheeler and five two-wheelers to a regiment; the Confederates two of each type. These proportions, however, do not appear to have been consistently adhered to. Because they frequently broke down, or were commandeered for other purposes, and because of the jarring, jolting rides which they afforded, the two-wheeled ambulances (nicknamed "avalanches" by the soldiers) were used less and less as the war progressed. Both armies suffered from shortage of ambulances throughout the war.

135. YANKEE HOSPITAL AT CHANCELLORSVILLE

Hospital on the Battlefield of Chancellorsville. Pencil drawing by Edwin Forbes. P

Field hospitals, such as this one, were located close to the battlefield but beyond the range of artillery fire, one or two miles to the rear. This one, with its log huts and surgeons operating out-of-doors, under canvas, was sketched by Forbes on May 2, 1863, "at the White House on the road to Ely's ford." Depicted are stretcher-bearers, coming and going, and a team of surgeons operating.

136. CONFEDERATE HOSPITAL AT CEDAR MOUNTAIN

Photograph by Timothy H. O'Sullivan, Aug. 1862.   P

This private dwelling served as a field hospital for some of the 1,100 Confederates who were wounded on August 9, 1862, when, during the 2d Bull Run campaign, Jackson defeated Banks at the battle of Cedar Run, Va., a few miles south of Culpeper.

137. TENT HOSPITALS IN THE WEST

"Hospital Varian, Hamburg, Tenn." Lithograph by Ehrgott, Forbriger & Co., Cincinnati, after A. E. Mathews, 31st Regt., O.V., U.S.A.   P

Small convalescent camps often were maintained to the rear of contending armies. This camp, with its rows of tents, was but one of the military hospitals at Hamburg which in the spring of 1862, when the sketch was made, were in charge of Dr. William Varian. The U.S. Sanitary Commission (Western Department) reported that in early May, after the Shiloh campaign, when it visited Hamburg (on the Tennessee River, a few miles above Pittsburg Landing), there were some 3,500 sick and wounded crowding the tents to capacity and more coming in each day. Many suffered, not from battle wounds, but from such illnesses as typhoid fever and scurvy. From camps such as these the worst cases were transferred to their States by hospital boats sent from such cities as Cincinnati, Ohio, Evansville, Ind., and Louisville, Ky.

138. CONFEDERATE CASUALTIES OF GETTYSBURG

"List of Men—Wounded & Sick Soldiers—in the Confederate States Hospital at the Roman Catholic Church, Williamsport, Md." Single-page manuscript document. From the Confederate Miscellany Collection.
                                                              MSS

Frequently, after major battles, the armies set up temporary hospitals in such structures as schools, churches, and private dwellings. After Gettysburg, for instance, the Confederates did so in the Roman Catholic Church at Williamsport, Md. This register, signed by Dr. "Wm. B. Wartford(?), Ass't. Surg. Act. in Charge," lists 28 Confederate soldiers wounded at Gettysburg between July 1 and 3. Among the total 38 listed when the record was prepared, are 17 described as "doing well," 9 "improving," 3 "not doing well," and 6 who "died" (between July 15 and 18).

139. A TYPICAL LOCAL RELIEF AGENCY

Hospital Scenes After the Battle of Gettysburg, July 1863. By the Patriot Daughters of Lancaster. [Lancaster, Pa.], 1864. From the George H. Stuart Papers.   MSS

Soldiers' aid and hospital relief societies sprang up almost immediately after the outbreak of the war. Some of these organizations were large (*e.g.*, the Women's Central Association of Relief in New York City), or they operated over a wide area (*e.g.*, the Women's Relief Society of the Confederate States in Nashville). The majority, however, were small local organizations (there were three in Atlanta, for instance), whose activities, in the South especially, were often integrated with those of larger State-wide organizations, supported by State and private funds. A leading example of the latter was the Georgia Relief and Hospital Association, organized in 1861.

The Patriot Daughters of Lancaster, one of the many local Societies in Pennsylvania, was organized on April 22, 1861, to provide clothing and nurses for the sick and the wounded. It sent relief supplies to Union troops after Antietam and Chancellorsville and later cared for 150 of the sick and wounded of Gettysburg. This pamphlet was published in order to raise funds to carry on its work.

140. NEW HOSPITALS FOR THE SICK AND WOUNDED

"Point Lookout, Md. View of Hammond Gen'l Hospital & U.S. Gen'l Depot for Prisoners of War." Colored lithograph by E. Sachse & Co., Baltimore, 1864.   P

By late 1861 it had become apparent to the Union Medical Department, prodded by the United States Sanitary Commission (*see* entry 194), that converted buildings alone would not suffice as hospitals and that, with new campaigns in the spring, more and larger hospitals would be needed to accommodate the sick and wounded. The Department, convinced by past experience of the desirability of segregating patients and providing for them large quantities of fresh air, decided to construct hospitals of new design, of the "pavilion" type, advocated by Dr. William A. Hammond. (This brilliant young doctor became Surgeon General by the spring of 1862.)

In 1862 a number of hospitals built on this design were completed throughout the country, among them the Mount Pleasant Hospital in Washington (*see* entry 127) and, at Point Lookout, on the Maryland side of the Potomac at Chesapeake Bay, the Hammond General Hospital. The latter, depicted in the lithograph below a summer hotel which also served as a hospital, consisted of 16 "pavilions", 175 feet long, radiating from a central circular passageway. One of these wings, larger than the rest, served as the administration building.

The prison camp shown (the enclosed area on the east or bay side of the peninsula) was established in the summer of 1863. Beyond it is the camp of the 5th New Hampshire Volunteers and to the west, on the Potomac, are the camps of the 2d and 12th New Hampshire Volunteers.

141. RICHMOND, CITY OF HOSPITALS

Photograph by unidentified photographer, Apr. 1865. (*See illustration.*)   P

The capital of the Confederacy was also its chief medical center, in or near which, according to the Richmond *Stranger's Guide and Official Directory* (1863), were 20 "hospitals for Confederate Soldiers." One of these was the famous Chimborazo Hospital, situated on a high hill overlooking the James River. Eventually numbering 150 wards, each housed in a separate one-story building 30 feet wide and 100 feet long and with a capacity of 40 to 60 patients, the establishment, said to be the largest military hospital in the world up to that time, began receiving patients early in 1862. Under Surgeon-in-Chief Dr. James B. McCaw, it is estimated that 76,000 patients were treated at Chimborazo during the Civil War.

142. SICKNESS IN THE CONFEDERATE ARMY

"Medical Director's Consolidated Report of Sick and Wounded of the Army Serving in W. Florida, Near Pensacola, for the Month of October 1861." Two-page printed document, with manuscript entries in ink. From the Confederate Miscellany Collection. MSS

Both Union and Confederate armies were incapacitated far more by the illnesses incurred by their troops than by the wounds which they suffered in battle. Among the most common ailments were those of the digestive system, especially intestinal disorders reported as diarrhea and dysentery. During the first 2 years of the war, 226,828 of 848,555 cases of disease entered in Confederate field reports east of the Mississippi were diagnosed as diarrhea-dysentery, and at Chimborazo about one in every five such cases was so reported.

This report on sickness in Bragg's army (11 regiments) during October 1861 reflects similar high incidence of intestinal disorder. Of 2,465 cases of specified disease reported, the highest totals are found under diarrhea and dysentery, for which there is a combined total of 590 cases—nearly one of every four.

143. THE VOLUNTEER NURSES OF THE WAR

Single-page holograph letter (retained copy) from Clara Barton to Abraham Lincoln, Feb. 1865. From the Barton Papers. MSS

The nursing of the Civil War, to a great extent, especially on the battlefield, was performed by men—soldiers and civilians. However, devoted women also sought to alleviate suffering occasioned by the war. The leading figures, to list but a few, include for the South: Juliet Hopkins; Ella Newsom; Phoebe Pember, who served as matron of a division (30 wards) of Chimborazo Hospital; and Sally Tompkins, the only woman commissioned in the Confederate Army and head of a hospital in Richmond which she equipped and maintained at her own expense. Outstanding in the North were "Mother" Mary Bickerdyke, nurse on the battlefields and in the hospitals of the west; reformer Dorothea Dix, who became superintendent of women nurses for the Union; Cornelia Hancock; Mary Safford; and Mary E. Walker, a nurse and physician who in the closing years of the war was commissioned an assistant surgeon. Notable also were the ministrations to both sides by the trained nurses of the Catholic sisterhoods, especially of the Sisters of Charity and the Sisters of Mercy.

Clara Barton, a clerk in the Patent Office at Washington when the war began, visited the battlefields, where occasionally she nursed, chiefly to distribute medical and other supplies which she had collected for the relief of sick and wounded soldiers. Late in the war President Lincoln, at her request (letter exhibited) assigned to her the task of corresponding with friends and relatives of missing prisoners and of preparing a list from burial and hospital records of those who had died during their confinement.

144. ONE OF WASHINGTON'S GENERAL HOSPITALS

Photograph by unidentified photographer.

P

The hospital center of the Union, as of the Confederacy, was its capital. In the summer of 1861, after 1st Bull Run, there were in the District of Columbia and its

"STORMING AND CAPTURE OF LOOKOUT MOUNTAIN." *Colored lithograph by Middleton, Strobridge & Co., Cincinnati.* (*See entry* 68.)

Head Qrs. in the Field, Va
8 am May 11th 1864.

Hon. E. M. Stanton,
Sec. of War. Washington D.C.

We have now entered the sixth day of very hard fighting. The result to this time is much in our favor. Our losses have been heavy as well as those of the enemy. I think the loss of the enemy must be greater. We have taken over five thousand prisoners, in battle, while he has taken from us but few except stragglers. I propose to fight it out on this line if it takes all summer.

U. S. Grant
Lieut. Gen. Comdg Armies

THE ACTION AT SPOTSYLVANIA. *Single-page holograph letter from Ulysses S. Grant to Edwin M. Stanton, May 11, 1864.* (*See entry 70.*)

"SHERIDAN'S ARMY FOLLOWING EARLY UP THE VALLEY OF THE SHENANDOAH."   *Pencil drawing by Alfred R. Waud.*   (*See entry 73.*)

SYMBOL OF WAR'S END. *Photograph by Timothy H. O'Sullivan, April 1865. (See entry 80.)*

List of Cargo for Confederate Government on Board the Economist bound for Nassau

10900	Long Enfield Rifles
540.	Short " "
10	Cases. " "
6	Cases Rifles
1	Case Carbines
11	Cases Revolvers
2800	Bayonet Scabbards
7000	Gun Sling
1000000	Percussion Caps
10480	Set of Accoutrement
21136	Blanket
16486	P. Shoes.
1757	" Boots
56328.	" Sock.
252	Set Harness
139	" Sadlery.
185	" Knapsack Board Gun Covers
250	Knapsack & Strap
2766	Great Coat
38	Cases Leather
10	" Farriers Tools
20	" Armourers "
3	" Sadlers "
1	" Thread do
12	" Trimmings do
5000	Friction Tubes
610	Gross Brass Buttons
700	Great Gross Trousir Buttons
526	Pieces Serge
1000	Drummers
24	Tarpaulings

"LIST OF CARGO FOR CONFEDERATE GOVERNMENT ON BOARD THE *Economist* BOUND FOR NASSAU." *Four-page document.* (*See entry 83.*)

"THE FIRST BATTLE BETWEEN 'IRON' SHIPS OF WAR." *Colored lithograph by Henry Bill, 1862.* *(See entry 86.)*

"THE BATTLE OF NEW ORLEANS." *Colored lithograph by T. Sinclair, Philadelphia. (See entry 88.)*

"THE CHARGE OF THE FIRST MARYLAND REGIMENT AT THE DEATH OF ASHBY." *Lithograph by A. Hoen & Co., Baltimore, 1862(?). (See entry 102.)*

"THE 21ST REG'T WISCONSIN VOL., CROSSING THE PONTOON BRIDGE, AT CINCINNATI." *Lithograph by Middleton, Strobridge & Co., Cincinnati.* (*See entry 105.*)

"FORT ALBANY, AT ARLINGTON HEIGHTS." *Colored lithograph by Murray & Co., 1862.* (*See entry 119.*)

"FORT SUMTER, DECEMBER 9TH, 1863." *Lithograph by J. Bien, New York, 1865(?).* (See entry 124.)

"U.S.A. GENL. HOSPITAL, LITTLE ROCK, ARKANSAS." Colored lithograph by A. Trochsler, Boston, 1864. (See entry 130.)

CHIMBORAZO HOSPITAL, RICHMOND. *Photograph by unidentified photographer, Apr. 1865.* (*See entry 141.*)

Ar. Sq. Jul 30 '65
Ward I
reb
John W. Morgan
age 18 – Shellot
Brunswick Co.
N. C.
gun shot wd rt leg above
knee
wound dog' well
been out nine months
Mrs.
Sarah A Morgan
(as above)

HOSPITAL NOTES BY WALT WHITMAN. *Holograph page from a Whitman notebook.* (*See entry 146.*)

COMBAT ARTIST ALFRED R. WAUD.   *Photograph by Timothy H. O'Sullivan, July 1863.   (See entry 147.)*

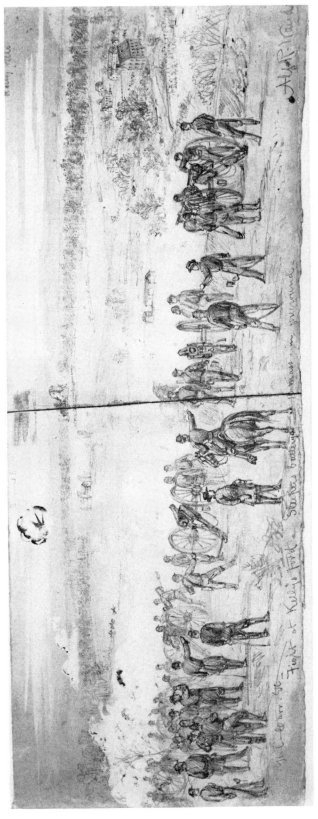

"FIGHT AT KELLY'S FORD, SLEEPER'S BATTERY 10TH MASS. IN FOREGROUND." *Drawing in pencil and Chinese white by Alfred R. Waud.*
(See entry 148.)

environs only 6 military hospitals, and these were small. By the end of 1864 there were 25 (the figure includes several in Alexandria and one at Point Lookout, Md.), many of which were "pavilion hospitals," constructed during the great building program of 1862 and 1863. (*See also* entries 127 and 140.)

Armory Square Hospital, one of the area's most famous, was constructed in the summer of 1862. Situated on a site selected for ease of access by water and by rail, it served for some time as a depot for sick and wounded from the Army of the Potomac. It consisted of a series of "pavilions" or wards (each with a capacity of 50 beds) placed parallel to each other. Behind it (to the left rear of the photograph) was the Columbian Arsenal, a three-story brick building, the rooms of which were partitioned to make additional wards. This building still stands near the northeast corner of 7th Street and Independence Avenue, SW.

145. WALT WHITMAN, SOJOURNER IN WASHINGTON

Photograph by Mathew B. Brady.   P

In December 1862, poet Walt Whitman came to Washington to find and care for his brother George, a Union soldier who had been hospitalized at Falmouth, Va. For the next 11 years "the good gray poet" remained in Washington, earning a livelihood as a government clerk and also, during the war years, devoting himself to volunteer nursing and visits with wounded soldiers hospitalized in and about the city. The war and the suffering it brought made a profound impression upon Whitman, to which he gave voice in *Drum-Taps*, a book of poems issued in 1865 as a tribute to the soldiers, and in his wartime letters to his mother, first published in 1898 under the title *The Wound Dresser*.

146. HOSPITAL NOTES MADE BY WHITMAN AT ARMORY SQUARE

Two holograph pages from a Walt Whitman notebook, both dated July 30, 1865, and headed "Arm. Sq. Ward I." From the Thomas B. Harned Collection.   MSS

As he visted the sick and wounded, Union and Confederate, Whitman jotted down reminders about the cases on scraps of paper or in little notebooks which he carried. Some were homemade affairs consisting of a few folded pieces of paper held together by a pin. These provided him with a memory record, and many served as rough material for future literary compositions, notably his prose work *Memoranda During the War* (1875). Some of the notes were brief, noting only the soldier's name, regiment and company, hospital, ward, and bed number. Others added such details as age, home address, mother's name, length of hospitalization, and the nature of the wound or illness.

These fragments from a Whitman notebook relate to "Thos. J. Byrd, age 19" and Confederate "John W. Morgan, age 18" (*see illustration*).

REPORTING THE WAR

The reporters of the war—the correspondent who wrote and the artist who sketched—were civilian employees of the great news media of the day, who accompanied the armies and, in the camp and on the battlefield, observed, described, and recorded what they saw. Among the leading combat

artists were Alfred R. Waud, Edwin Forbes, Arthur Lumley, and Frank Vizetelly. Examples of their work are to be found throughout this publication, as well as those of pictorial reporters of another kind—the war photographers, among whom were Mathew B. Brady, Alexander Gardner, Timothy H. O'Sullivan, and James Gibson.

The artist enjoyed a distinct advantage over the photographer, who, while he could report much more realistically and accurately, labored under the handicap of having to use glass plates and to make long time-exposures. Unable to photograph live action successfully, he had to content himself with "stills" taken in the camp and on the field after battle. The combat artist worked under no such restriction. Moreover, drawings reproduced as woodcuts were the only method of illustration available to the pictorial weeklies, the technique of photo-engraving not as yet having been developed. It was to be many years before the general public was to see the thousands of scenes recorded by Brady and other photographers during the war.

The press, North and South, did remarkably well in informing the public of the progress of the war, but it furnished a major problem to the military, for far too often it revealed valuable information to the opposing side.

147. FLETCHER HARPER'S COMBAT ARTISTS

Photograph by Timothy H. O'Sullivan, July 1863. (*See illustration.*)　　　　P

The leading newspapers and illustrated weeklies maintained professional artists ("specials") on the battlefields and in the camps, where they produced sketches for publication as wood engravings. Foremost of these periodicals was *Harper's Weekly,* which had on its staff such celebrated combat artists as Alfred R. Waud, Theodore R. Davis, Alexander Simplot, and, during 1864–65, William Waud.

London-born Alfred R. Waud, generally regarded as the greatest of the Civil War newspaper artists, came to the United States

in 1850. His first war sketches were drawn for the *New York Illustrated News* in 1861. The following year he became a "special artist" for *Harper's Weekly,* and he made sketches for that publication of the campaigns of the Army of the Potomac for the duration of the war. The photograph, showing him in all of his magnificence at Gettysburg, is reminiscent of an English correspondent's description of him as:

Blue-eyed, fair-bearded, strapping and stalwart, full of loud, cheery laughs and comic songs, armed to the teeth, jack-booted, gauntleted, slouch-hatted, yet clad in the shooting-jacket of a civilian . . .

148. FROM SKETCH TO PUBLISHED ENGRAVING

(1) "Fight at Kelly's Ford, Sleeper's Battery 10th Mass. in Foreground." Drawing in pencil and Chinese white by Alfred R. Waud (*see illustration*); (2) "The Army of the Potomac—Fight at Kelly's Ford, Sleeper's Massachusetts Battery in the Fore-Ground." Photocopy of wood engraving in *Harper's Weekly,* Dec. 5, 1863, after Alfred R. Waud.
　　　　P

In general the published woodcuts faithfully reproduced the pictorial elements of the artists' original compositions. In some instances, however, the drawings as they left the artists' hands were incomplete or, perhaps, obscure in certain details. It then became necessary for the artist who copied the drawing on the block to finish the scene. This Waud drawing of Jacob H. Sleeper's 6-gun battery in action at Kelly's Ford is a case in point. Beyond the heads of the group of officers to left (Gen. Joseph B. Carr and staff), Waud has indistinctly rendered a gun and four cannoneers; the home artist has omitted the gun and rendered the soldiers as bystanders. In other essentials, such as the number of soldiers, the positions they assume, and the movements of each, the drawing and the cut are identical.

149. A SOLDIER-ARTIST'S CONTRIBUTION TO *HARPER'S*

"The Thirty-First Regiment Ohio Volunteers (Colonel Walker) Crossing the Kentucky River at Boone's Knob, October 2, 1861." Photocopy of wood engraving in *Harper's Weekly*, Nov. 23, 1861, after Alfred E. Mathews.   P

Another source of the illustrations which appeared in the picture weeklies, especially early in the war before their staffs of field artists had been fully developed, was the soldier-artist. It is estimated that 314 such artists known by name supplied 673 published drawing to the "big three" of *Harper's*, *Frank Leslie's*, and the *New York Illustrated News*. Alfred E. Mathews submitted to *Harper's* two sketches relating to the war in Kentucky (as far as is known, the only drawings he ever sent), both of which were published and one of which is exhibited.

150. FRANK LESLIE'S COMBAT ARTISTS

"My Studio." Pencil drawing by Edwin Forbes.   P

Chief rival of *Harper's Weekly* as the principal pictorial periodical covering the Civil War was *Frank Leslie's Illustrated Newspaper*, which had among its array of artists Edwin Forbes, Henri Lovie, Arthur Lumley, Francis H. Schell, William T. Crane, and, for the first 2 years of the war, William Waud.

The combat artist who drew for Harper or Leslie traveled with the armies, sharing the dangers and hardships of the soldier. In winter quarters he could manage to obtain relatively comfortable accommodations—a hut perhaps, or possibly a tent with brush windbreak and crude stove, such as is depicted in Forbes' "studio," sketched by him at Rappahannock Station on March 17, 1864.

Forbes was assigned by Leslie to the Army of the Potomac, which he joined in 1862 at the age of 23.

151. A BRITISH ARTIST-CORRESPONDENT IN THE SOUTH

Photograph by Mathew B. Brady, 1861 or 1862. (*See illustration.*)   P

Frank Vizetelly was the only "special artist" to accompany Confederate forces, not for a Southern journal but on behalf of *The Illustrated London News*, which sent him in the spring of 1861 to cover "the war in America." At first he accompanied the Northern armies, but late in the summer of 1862, chafing at restrictions imposed by the Federal high command—at a time, moreover, when the Union cause was less favorably regarded in England—he turned to the South. That he did so was fortunate, for, as has been observed: "More than 130 of Vizetelly's drawings were published in the *Illustrated London News*, and together they comprise the principal contemporary record in pictures of the Confederate War effort" (*The Civil War: a Centennial Exhibition of Eyewitness Drawings*, Washington, D.C., National Gallery of Art, 1961).

The South *did* have its artists. Their sketches, however, remained largely unpublished, since there were in the Confederacy no great pictorial weeklies such as those put out by Harper and Leslie in New York. An attempt in Richmond to meet the need for such a publication resulted in the appearance in September 1862 of *The Southern Illustrated News*. Patterned after its London counterpart, this periodical could not afford to maintain a staff of artists, was unable to find competent engravers, ran into shortages of paper and other supplies, and finally in November 1864 was forced to cease publication.

152. A FAMOUS BRITISH WAR CORRESPONDENT VISITS AMERICA

William Howard Russell. *My Diary North and South*. New York, 1863. Opened to frontispiece: Woodcut of Russell seated at a writing desk.   G

The first of the war correspondents, William Howard Russell of the London *Times,* early in 1861 was sent to observe and report on the unrest in the United States. On March 28 the noted journalist, whom Margaret Leech has described as "a portly, graying and quietly dandified Briton," was a guest at the first state dinner given by President and Mrs. Lincoln. Following a tour of the South, he returned to Washington in time to witness the Union debacle at 1st Bull Run, after which he filed the celebrated dispatch which was to earn him the sobriquet of "Bull Run Russell" and so embitter the North that shortly thereafter he returned to London. *My Diary North and South,* an account of his experience in the States, appeared in 1863. Displayed is a one-volume American edition published by Harper.

153. CONFEDERATE PROPAGANDA IN EUROPE

Henry Hotze letterbook, Nov. 14, 1861, to Dec. 31, 1863. Opened to "The C.S. State Department Service Fund in Account with Henry Hotze, Commercial Agent at London, Jan. 1 to Dec. 31, 1863." From the Hotze Papers.   MSS

On May 1, 1862, Henry Hotze, a Confederate agent in London (*see* entry 173), and a former Southern journalist, founded *The Index,* a self-styled "weekly journal of politics, literature, and news, devoted to the exposition of the mutual interests, political and commercial, of Great Britain and the Confederate States of America." Subsidized by the Confederate Government, this publication provided a Southern viewpoint of events, political and military, taking place across the sea. At a time when the European public was getting its news of the war chiefly from Northern papers, Hotze labored assiduously, especially among British editors, journalists, and people of influence in society and government, to create an atmosphere favorable to the Confederacy. A copy of a letter in this volume (September 26, 1862,

to Secretary of State Judah P. Benjamin) shows that many of the contributors to *The Index* were Englishmen, among them the talented Percy Greg, columnist for the *Saturday Review.*

The first entry of the pages displayed records a subsidy of £1,995 to *The Index* for the period October 23, 1862, to December 31, 1863.

154. NEWSMEN IN ACTION

"The Press on the Field." Photocopy of wood engraving in *Harper's Weekly,* Apr. 30, 1864, after Thomas Nast.   P

By 1860, Thomas Nast, a youth of 21, had already worked for *Frank Leslie's, The New York Illustrated News,* and *The Illustrated London News.* In 1861 he covered Garibaldi's Italian campaign. In 1862 he joined the art staff of *Harper's,* but he saw little service in the field during the course of the war. Preferring to draw pictures with ideas rather than scenes of battle, and encouraged to do so by Harper, he became a skilled propagandist and political cartoonist. His wartime sketches had tremendous influence upon the masses, so much so that Lincoln is reported to have said: "Thomas Nast has been our best recruiting sergeant." In later years he achieved great fame for his popularization of the Tammany tiger, the Democratic donkey, and the Republican elephant.

"The Press on the Field" is a series of small sketches depicting the press "in action." Typical of Nast's style, with overtones of pathos and sly humor, are his drawings of war correspondents gathering "contraband news" from refugee Negroes and "reliable information" from camp ne'er-do-wells.

155. NEWSPAPER GIANT

Photograph by Timothy H. O'Sullivan, Aug. 1863.   P

Dominating the American newspaper scene during the war were the New York dailies, foremost of which were Horace Greeley's *Tribune,* Henry J. Raymond's *Times,* poet William Cullen Bryant's *Evening Post,* and James Gordon Bennett's *Herald.* The most massively organized was the *Herald,* which spent more than $500,000 on war news during the conflict. It has been estimated that at least 63 correspondents of the *Herald* were in the field at one time or another during the war. In the Army of the Potomac it had correspondents with each division and, in addition, *Herald* tents and a wagon with each corps. Shown are its tents and wagon ("headquarters") at Bealeton, Va., in the summer of 1863.

156. A WAR CORRESPONDENT WHO BECAME LIBRARIAN OF CONGRESS

(1) Single-page holograph pass for John R. Young, July 20, 1861, signed by Simon Cameron (*see illustration*); (2) Two-page holograph letter from Simon Cameron to Irvin McDowell, July 20, 1861. From the John Russell Young Papers.   MSS

Among the Northern correspondents (they called themselves "the Bohemian Brigade") were such outstanding reporters as the prolific Charles Carleton Coffin of the Boston *Journal,* Joseph B. ("Mack") McCullough of the Cincinnati *Gazette,* Lorenzo L. Crounse of the New York *Times,* George A. Townsend ("Gath") of the New York *Herald,* Henry Villard of the New York *Tribune,* and George W. Smalley, also of the *Tribune,* noted for his remarkable description of the battle of Antietam. In such distinguished circles moved John Russell Young of John W. Forney's Philadelphia *Press.*

A copy boy with the *Press* in 1857, Young soon became a reporter. During the war he was assigned to the Army of the Potomac (1861–62), and later he covered Banks' Red River campaign (1864). In 1862 he became managing editor of Forney's two daily newspapers—the *Press* and the Washington *Daily Morning Chronicle.* After the

war he continued his editorial and journalistic career, accompanied former President Grant on a trip around the world in 1879, served as minister to China, and in 1897 was appointed by President McKinley to be the seventh Librarian of Congress, a position which he held until his death in 1899.

The documents displayed relate to 1st Bull Run, Young's initial assignment as a war correspondent. His report of the defeat and retreat of the Federal forces there is generally regarded as one of the better accounts to appear in the Northern press. Written by the Secretary of War, Simon Cameron, the day before the battle, the pass was intended to get Young through the lines to McDowell's headquarters. In the accompanying letter, Cameron wrote:

Have just returned and arranged to send you some help tomorrow a.m. The young gentleman, Jno. R. Young, who hands you this, is connected with Forney's Press in Philadelphia and goes to the Army in his vocation, but I feel a more than common interest in himself, and therefore will esteem it a personal favor if you will turn him over to one of the Brigadiers, who will extend to him the hospitalities of his military family. You will also direct the quartermaster to furnish Mr. Young a horse and equipments.

157. "A WELCOME VISITOR"

Photograph by Alexander Gardner, Nov. 1863.   P

At a camp somewhere in Virginia, a newspaper vendor, with cart and horse, hawks copies of *Harper's Weekly* and other "Philadelphia, New York, and Baltimore papers."

158. "EXTRA! EXTRA!"

"Mississippian Extra. Mississipian Office, Aug. 8—9 a.m. Malvern Hill taken by the Enemy. [etc.]" [Jackson, Miss., 1862]. Broadside. From the Alfred Whital Stern Collection.   R

In North and South, extras such as this one published by the *Daily Mississippian* in Jackson kept the public informed of the progress of the war on the various fronts. Based upon news dispatches of August 6 and 7, 1862, from Richmond and Knoxville, it announces a minor defeat in Virginia ("Malvern Hill taken by the Enemy"), reports unrest in the North ("The North Depressed," "Anti-War Meetings Being Held," "Recruiting a Failure at the North"), and claims success for Confederate forces in the West ("Good News from Tennessee," "Battle near Tazwell," "Confederates Victorious," "Enemy Repulsed with Great Slaughter," "They are in Full Retreat," "The Army of East Tennessee Captured"). (For examples of other wartime newspaper extras, *see* entries 5 and 48.)

159. MATHEW B. BRADY, WARTIME PHOTOGRAPHER IN THE NORTH

Photograph by unidentified photographer, July 1861. (*See illustration.*)　　P

When the war broke out, Mathew B. Brady, already one of the country's leading portrait photographers, with studios in Washington and New York, undertook the ambitious project of preparing a camera record of the war, a venture which was to spell his financial ruin but make him the best-known of Civil War photographers. With the approval of the Union army, he organized and sent out to the camps and the battlefields teams of photographers—as many as 20 or more at the height of the war. Foremost of the photographers whom he hired were Alexander Gardner, George N. Barnard, James F. Gibson, and Timothy H. O'Sullivan. Brady seldom photographed in the field, his work being confined chiefly to the beginning of the war and to camps and battlefields about Washington. This photograph of Brady in a smock was taken, probably in his studio on July 22, 1861, after his return from Bull Run.

160. PHOTOGRAPHERS IN THE FIELD

Photograph by unidentified photographer.
　　P

Brady sent his field photographers out in pairs with helpers. One such "team" is seen here beside their photographic wagon—a buggy with makeshift darkroom of canvas and boxes (stenciled "Brady") in which to store glass plates.

161. "THE CONFEDERATE BRADY"

Single-page holograph letter from Walter Dinsmore to George S. Cook, Jan. 11, 1861. From the Cook Papers.　　MSS

Among the photographers who worked for the South were A. D. Lytle, George Armstead, Julian Vannerson, J. D. Edwards (*see* entry 20), and George S. Cook, of Charleston, S.C., onetime Brady employee, who became the chief combat photographer of the Confederacy.

The letter displayed represents an attempt by a Philadelphia photographic gallery (Walter Dinsmore & Co.) to exploit the popularity of Maj. Robert Anderson, who at the time was in command of the defenses of Charleston Harbor. A few days before (December 26) Anderson had transferred the garrison at Fort Moultrie to the more defensible Fort Sumter. The letter reads:

As Major Anderson is quite popular North, I think that we might make considerable money, if we had his picture. If you can procure us a ½ plate Ambrotype of him, we will copy it into Photographs and divide the profits accrueing from the sale. Answer soon, delays are dangerous; the furore may wear off.

162. THE "HERO OF FORT SUMTER"

Photograph by George S. Cook, 1861.

Maj. Robert Anderson, U.S.A., whose portrait Dinsmore wished to sell in the North. (*See* entry 161.) Whether or not Cook responded we do not know.

POLITICS AND GOVERNMENT

The course of the war and its outcome were shaped and determined by the governments of the nations as well as by their armies. Some of the problems confronting the political leaders, North and South, were similar in nature, if not in degree. Both administrations were faced with the task of financing the war; both Presidents met with internal opposition; and foreign relations were largely centered on gaining, or preventing, recognition of the Confederacy by European powers. Other problems were unique. The paradox of increasing the authority of a central government in a nation established on the doctrine of States rights placed Jefferson Davis often in conflict with State authorities. President Lincoln's great problem was to place and maintain the support of the war on as broad a popular base as possible; and his great domestic test was the election of 1864, one of the most critical in American history. Inextricably involved in the problems to be met was the overriding moral issue of human slavery.

163. POLITICAL LEADERS OF THE UNION

"The First Reading of the Emancipation Proclamation Before the Cabinet." Mezzotint by Alexander H. Ritchie, 1866, after a painting by F. B. Carpenter. (*See illustration.*) P

The Republican party was largely composed of former Whigs and Democrats; and political antecedents as well as geography helped determine the selection of President Lincoln's Cabinet, shown here as it appeared in 1862. Seated, from left to right, are: Edwin M.

Stanton of Pittsburgh and Washington, Secretary of War, who replaced Simon Cameron in January 1862; President Lincoln; Gideon Welles of Connecticut, a former editor who served capably as Secretary of the Navy and was sometimes called "Father Neptune" by the President; William H. Seward of New York, Secretary of State, who as leader of the Republican Party had expected to receive the nomination which went to Lincoln and was early dissuaded from the notion that he, and not the President, would lead the Administration; and Edward Bates of Missouri, the Attorney General, who had also been a candidate for the nomination in 1860. Standing are: Salmon P. Chase of Ohio, Secretary of the Treasury, who had Presidential ambitions; Caleb B. Smith of Indiana, Secretary of the Interior; and Montgomery Blair of Missouri and Maryland, member of a powerful political family, who as Postmaster General brought about numerous advances in the postal system, including the first free delivery of mail in cities.

164. AN EARLY INCOME TAX SUPPORTS THE WAR

"Income Tax for 1862." [Washington, D.C.(?), 1863] Four-page printed document (instructions and blank). R

The financing problem of the Federal Government during the war was met in part by the issuing of paper currency, popularly known as "Greenbacks" or "shin plasters," for amounts below a dollar. As the war progressed, however, income from increased taxes rose sharply. Among the new taxes was a Federal income tax. Enacted as an emergency measure, the tax was levied in 1862 and continued until 1872.

165. POLITICAL LEADERS OF THE CONFEDERACY

"Jefferson Davis and His Cabinet, with General Lee in the Council Chamber at Richmond." Lithograph by Thomas Kelly, New York, 1866. (*See illustration.*) P

The Confederate Cabinet reflected President Davis' desire for the support of all the States of the Confederacy. Six of the seven which had seceded by March 1861 were represented, the exception being the President's home State of Mississippi. Beset by obstacles inherent to the war and disturbed by some personal jealousies and conflicts, the Cabinet changed in its composition several times. Of the original members shown, only three—Mallory, Benjamin, and Reagan— were in office at the close of the war. Pictured, from left to right, are: Stephen R. Mallory of Florida, the very able Secretary of the Navy; Judah P. Benjamin of Louisiana, originally appointed Attorney General, who later served as Secretary of War and of State; Leroy P. Walker of Alabama, Secretary of War, who resigned in September 1861 to accept a commission as a brigadier general; President Jefferson Davis; Gen. Robert E. Lee; John H. Reagan of Texas, Postmaster General, who served also as Secretary of the Treasury; Christopher G. Memminger of South Carolina, a German-born orphan who became Secretary of the Treasury; Vice President Alexander H. Stephens of Georgia, never a truly active participant in the administration; and Robert Toombs of Georgia, an outspoken critic of the administration who reluctantly accepted the post of Secretary of State, an office he held for only a few months.

166. THE CONFEDERATE CAPITAL MOVES NORTH

"The Capitol of the C.S., Richmond, Va." Colored lithograph by E. Sachse & Co., 1865.   P

In May 1861, Virginia having joined the Confederacy, the Confederate Congress, overriding a veto of President Davis, voted to transfer the seat of government from Montgomery, Ala., to Richmond, where it met in the old Jefferson-designed State Capitol building.

167. COTTON SUPPORTS THE CONFEDERACY

"Subscriptions of Crop for Defense of the Confederate States. Confederate States of America, May 20th, 1861." Broadside form, filled in. From the Confederate Miscellany Collection.   MSS

Cotton was the greatest resource of the Confederacy and the means by which it hoped to support its credit abroad. In exchange for newly issued bonds, citizens of the Confederate States subscribed portions of their crops to the government. The cotton was then sold in foreign markets and the money used to purchase supplies unavailable elsewhere. Exhibited is a document showing subscriptions of crops in Mobile, Ala.

168. A CONFEDERATE GENERAL REASSURES THE PUBLIC

Headquarters, Department of Western Virginia, Charleston, Va., Sept. 24, 1862. General Order no. —. Broadside.   R

No problem facing the Confederacy was greater than that of adequate financing. Revenue was largely derived from the issue of bonds and treasury notes, of which large amounts were printed (some in New York City) in 1861 and 1862. On September 23, 1862, Congress authorized the unlimited issue of paper money to cover appropriations. It failed in its later attempts to control the resulting inflation, to which also the rising shortages of commodities contributed. By the end of the war Confederate currency was almost worthless. In the broadside shown, issued the day after the action of Congress, Maj. Gen. W. W. Loring assures the public of the security of Confederate money.

169. AN ELECTION IN THE CONFEDERACY

"Virginia Electoral Ticket. Election November 6th, 1861. For President, Jefferson

Davis, of Mississippi. For Vice-President, Alex. H. Stephens, of Georgia." [Richmond(?), 1861]. Broadside. R

In February 1861, Jefferson Davis and Alexander H. Stephens became the President and Vice President of the Confederate States of America by action of the Provisional Congress. In the fall of that year they were duly elected to those offices by a vote of the people. This electoral ticket names the candidates, Davis and Stephens, together with electors for the State at large and for Virginia's 16 districts.

170. JEFFERSON DAVIS IS INAUGURATED AGAIN

"Programme for the Inauguration of the President and Vice-President of the Confederate States." [Richmond(?), 1862]. Four-page printed document. From the Confederate Miscellany Collection. MSS

On February 18, 1862, the permanent constitution of the Confederate States went into effect. On that day also Jefferson Davis and Alexander H. Stephens were formally inaugurated as President and Vice President, to serve a single term of six years. The "programme" lists the order of the inaugural ceremonies and the persons invited to attend.

171. A CONFEDERATE PASSPORT

Confederate States of America. Department of State. Passport for Stephen C. Michell, June 20, 1861. Broadside form, filled in. From the Confederate Miscellany Collection. MSS

Agents and representatives of the Confederacy abroad were numerous, energetic, and skillful. Many of the States, and even private businesses, also had agents representing their interests in Europe, Mexico, the West Indies, and Canada. These men, who served a variety of purposes both political and commercial, traveled as citizens of the new

nation. Shown is a passport of the Confederate States of America, signed by Secretary of State Robert A. Toombs.

172. THE TRENT AFFAIR

"The Seizure by Captain Wilks [sic], of the United States' War-Ship San Jacinto, of Messrs. Slidell and Mason, Confederate Commissioners, on Board the British Mail-Steamer Trent." Photocopy of wood engraving in The Illustrated London News, Dec. 7, 1861. (See illustration.) P

In the fall of 1861 an incident off the coast of Cuba seriously endangered relations between the United States and Great Britain. On November 8, Charles Wilkes, commanding the U.S.S. San Jacinto, stopped the British steamer Trent and removed two of her passengers, James M. Mason and John Slidell, Confederate commissioners bound for Great Britain and France. The Trent was allowed to proceed, but Mason and Slidell were arrested and later imprisoned at Fort Warren in Boston harbor. The Northern public, Congress (the House of Representatives voted Wilkes a gold medal), and a majority of the Cabinet rejoiced. President Lincoln, however, was cautious and through William H. Seward, Secretary of State, instructed Charles Francis Adams, Minister to London, to inform the British that Wilkes had acted on his own initiative. News of the incident in England produced great indignation and even demands for war. A note demanding an apology and immediate release of the men was presented. On December 26 Seward agreed to "cheerfully" liberate the prisoners, realizing that the alternative was probably war. To placate American public opinion and to satisfy the demands of the British, Seward based his action on the grounds that Wilkes had not brought the Trent affair before a court of adjudication and had thereby violated the American principle of freedom of the seas.

173. TWO CONFEDERATE AGENTS ABROAD

Single-page holograph letter from John Slidell to Henry Hotze, Paris, Oct. 15, 1864. From the Hotze Papers.   MSS

Two of the most active Confederate representatives abroad are represented in this letter. John Slidell of Louisiana, after his release from Fort Warren (*see* entry 172), reached Paris as a commissioner to the government of Napoleon III. Although he was never received officially, Slidell in private meetings with the French monarch enlisted his sympathies for the Southern cause. However, little, if any, active aid came to the Confederacy as a result of these meetings. Henry Hotze, the recipient of the letter, served as the chief propagandist of the Confederate States. As founder and editor of *The Index,* published in London, Hotze worked energetically to present the Confederate viewpoint to European readers. In the letter displayed, Slidell requests copies of the State map of Virginia and asks a question about the blockade.

174. THE LAIRD RAMS

Single-page holograph letter from Thomas H. Dudley to Gideon Welles, Sept. 5, 1863. From the Henry Hotze Papers.   MSS

In the fall of 1863 two ironclad steamers, designed for use against the Federal blockade, brought the United States dangerously close to war with Great Britain. Known as the Laird Rams after their builder, John Laird and Sons of Birkenhead, England, these vessels were ordered in the summer of 1862 by Confederate naval agent James D. Bulloch. Fearing that they would be seized by the British before they could put to sea, John Slidell arranged for their transfer to a French firm which would resell them to the Confederacy when they were safely beyond British jurisdiction. Union diplomats in England, notably Charles Francis Adams,

Minister at London, kept careful watch on the progress being made on the rams and worked assiduously to prevent their sailing. The vessels were launched in the summer of 1863, and on September 1 Lord John Russell, British Foreign Secretary, informed Adams that the British could not interfere. Adams replied in a letter on September 5: "It would be superfluous in me to point out to your lordship that this is war." Russell, however, 2 days earlier had ordered the vessels detained, suspecting their eventual destination and probably influenced by Union victories at Gettysburg and Vicksburg. In the letter exhibited, Thomas H. Dudley, United States Consul at Liverpool, reports to the Secretary of the Navy:

Supposing it important that you should have a sketch of the Rams building at Lairds for the Rebels I procured an artist to go in the yard and make one. He had great difficulty but at last succeeded. I enclose it to you. . . . The prevailing opinion here is that they will let them sail. The armament will consist of 6 guns two in each Turret & two in the stern. I have not learned their caliber. They are Blakley guns.

The presence of this document in the Henry Hotze papers suggests the possibility that it was intercepted by the Confederates.

175. THE FAILURE OF CONFEDERATE DIPLOMACY

"Not Any, we Thank You Mr. Davis." Lithographic cartoon by Ehrgott, Forbriger & Co., 1861. (*See illustration.*)   P

The object of Confederacy diplomacy was to secure recognition as an independent nation and if possible, bring about foreign intervention to break the Federal blockade. Confederate agents failed almost completely in their efforts. Early in the war Great Britain recognized the Confederacy as a belligerent, but recognition as a nation and foreign intervention remained forlorn hopes throughout the conflict. Sympathy for the Southern cause existed among the aristocracy in both Great Britain and France; but the masses remained largely pro-Union, in spite of the great distress caused by the cotton famine in

British milling centers. Favorable commercial treaties were offered both European nations by the Confederacy; but active, forthright support was never forthcoming. A French offer of mediation, made early in 1863 and flatly rejected by William H. Seward, was followed by a shifting of sympathies to the Union. As Napoleon's hope of having an independent Confederacy bordering the empire he hoped to establish in Mexico dwindled, even the social acceptance which the Confederates had once enjoyed lessened. The cartoon depicts Napoleon III rejecting Confederate overtures.

176. THE EMANCIPATION
PROCLAMATION

Two-page holograph document by Abraham Lincoln [July 22, 1862]. From the Robert Todd Lincoln Collection.   MSS

Abraham Lincoln, personally opposed to slavery but aware also of the need to keep the Border States within the Union and of the legal limitations upon the subject, proceeded slowly with the problem. An advocate of compensated emancipation, he drew upon his powers as Commander-in-Chief (perhaps illegally) to issue the most powerful and effective state paper of the war. Issued as a military measure, the Emancipation Proclamation, Lincoln wrote, was intended "to practically restore . . . the constitutional relation between the general government, and each, and all, the states, wherein that relation is now suspended, or disturbed." This fundamental document proclaimed that on January 1, 1863, "all persons held as slaves within any state or states, wherein the constitutional authority of the United States shall not then be practically recognized, submitted to, and maintained, shall then, thenceforward, and forever, be free." Lincoln first drafted the proclamation and presented it to his Cabinet in July 1862, but upon the advice of William H. Seward, he withheld it until the military situation became more favorable. On September 22, 1862, 5 days after the Battle of Antietam, where Lee was repulsed in his invasion of Maryland, the preliminary proclamation appeared. Shown is Lincoln's draft of the proclamation "as first sketched and shown to the Cabinet in July 1862."

177. LINCOLN PREPARING THE
PROCLAMATION

"President Lincoln, Writing the Proclamation of Freedom, January 1st, 1863." Colored lithograph by Ehrgott, Forbriger & Co., Cincinnati, 1864, after painting by Blythe.
P

With the Emancipation Proclamation Abraham Lincoln gave the war new dimensions of morality and human freedom which are suggested in the allegorical lithograph shown. Among the symbols which the artist uses to depict some of the principles which he imagined influenced Lincoln in preparing the proclamation are the Bible, a scale of justice, and a copy of the Presidential oath.

178. THE PROCLAMATION REACHES
THE SOUTH

"Reading the Emancipation Proclamation." Engraving by J. W. Watts, 1864, after H. W. Herrick. (See illustration.)   P

The Emancipation Proclamation had vast and practical consequences. In Europe the masses overwhelmingly approved Lincoln's action, and their support effectively ended any chance of intervention by their governments on behalf of the Confederacy, which, by its continued resistance, was placed in the untenable position of appearing to fight to preserve slavery. Within the South slaves flocked into the Federal lines as the armies advanced, depriving the Confederacy of much of the laboring force it so desperately needed to support its armies. The engraving depicts a Union soldier reading the proclamation to a group of slaves.

179. THE THIRTEENTH AMENDMENT

Single-page holograph document, an engrossed copy of the submitting resolution of the Thirteenth Amendment, signed by Abraham Lincoln and others, [February 1, 1865]. MSS

President Lincoln was denounced by many in the North because the Emancipation Proclamation freed only those slaves within the Confederacy and did not permanently end slavery as an institution. The Thirteenth Amendment to the Constitution, an engrossed copy of which is displayed, abolished forever human slavery within the United States and its territories. A Congressional resolution calling for the amendment failed to pass the House of Representatives in June 1864, and in a message to Congress delivered the following December Lincoln asked again for the legislation. The Senate approved in January 1865, and on the last day of the month, with a shrewd political assist from the President, the resolution carried in the House. Submitted to the States, the Amendment obtained the necessary three-fourths vote (in which eight of the former Confederate States joined) and was ratified on December 18, 1865.

180. THE NEGRO IN THE WAR

" 'Mustered Out' Colored Volunteers Arriving at Little Rock, Ark." Drawing in pencil and Chinese white by Alfred R. Waud. P

Negro soldiers, who had served in both the Revolution and War of 1812, were, at the beginning, reluctantly accepted into the Union army. Gens. David H. Hunter and Benjamin F. Butler, in South Carolina and New Orleans, made early attempts to enlist them, but large-scale recruiting did not occur until mid-1863. Rhode Island, Kansas, and Massachusetts were among the first States to call for Negro troops, and in April 1863 Lincoln authorized the acceptance of four such regiments. By the end of the war every State in the Union, including those then within the Confederacy, had furnished Negro soldiers. Nearly 300,000 Negroes served in the Union armies and participated in such engagements as Milliken's Bend, The Crater (at Petersburg), and Fort Pillow. Waud's drawing of Negro soldiers returning home after the war was reproduced as a wood engraving in *Harper's Weekly,* May 19, 1866.

181. NEGROES AND THE CONFEDERATE ARMY

Single-page holograph letter from R. T. Johnston, Jr., to John C. Breckenridge, March 28, 1865. From the Confederate Miscellany Collection. MSS

Early in the war a regiment of free Negroes was organized in New Orleans, but it was never accepted for service. In January 1864, a proposal to arm the slaves and guarantee them their freedom for their service was suppressed by President Davis, who, however, by the following November reconsidered the matter. General Lee, aware of the desperate situation of his army, stressed the importance of the proposal, and in March 1865 the Confederate Congress passed legislation authorizing the President to call for Negro troops, with, however, no provision made for their emancipation. A few companies were organized in Richmond, but the surrender at Appomattox prevented what has been described as "the ironic spectacle of Negroes fighting for the cause of Southern independence and the perpetuation of their own bondage." In this letter the Captain of Company "I" of the 7th Alabama Cavalry requests permission from the Confederate Secretary of War to organize a regiment of Negroes under the recent legislation of Congress.

182. GENERALS AND CONGRESSIONAL COMMITTEES

Single-page manuscript note, unsigned. From the Benjamin F. Wade Papers. MSS

President Lincoln often found himself opposed and harassed by the powerful Joint

Committee on the Conduct of the War, several of whose members later played a leading role in shaping reconstruction policies. This Committee, of which Senator Wade of Ohio was chairman, performed valuable services for the Union, but it also injected a spirit of extreme political partisanship into its investigations of military affairs. Generals suspected of lacking enthusiasm for abolition, usually of Democratic antecedents, were mercilessly and skillfully attacked; other commanders of correct political sentiments were favored. George B. McClellan was a principal target, as was Don Carlos Buell. In this note sent to Wade, the latter is described as "a d - - d little squirt—without brains enough for a cock-sparrow. He is even a smaller man than McClelan [*sic*]— and that is getting down almighty low. God Save the Republic! If *He* won't—the thing is already in Hell."

183. COPPERHEADS AND HABEAS CORPUS

Single-page holograph letter from Abraham Lincoln to Edwin M. Stanton, May 13, 1863. From the Stanton Papers.　　　MSS

Two of the most vexing of the domestic problems which faced the Lincoln administration are reflected in this letter from Lincoln to Stanton. In both the Union and Confederacy, there were elements who opposed the war and sometimes worked against its successful prosecution. The Northern movement, largely centered in Ohio, Indiana, and Southern Illinois, had as its head Clement L. Vallandigham, an Ohio Congressman. This leader of the "Copperheads," as they were called, promoted resistance to conscription, defied the army in speeches in Ohio, and on May 4 was arrested by Gen. Ambrose E. Burnside. Tried by a Military commission, he was imprisoned in Fort Warren. The resulting furor focused attention on Lincoln's proclamations sus-

pending the Writ of Habeas Corpus in cases of military necessity, actions which had received considerable criticism in the North. On May 19, by Lincoln's direction, Vallandigham was banished beyond the Federal military lines. In the letter exhibited, Lincoln writes:

Since parting with you I have seen the Secretaries of State and the Treasury, and they both think we better not issue the special suspension of the Writ of Habeas Corpus spoken of. Gov. Chase thinks the case is not before Judge Swaine, that it is before Judge Levett, that the writ will probably not issue, whichever the application may be before; and that, in no event, will Swaine commit an imprudence. His chief reason for thinking the writ will not issue, is that he has seen in a newspaper that Judge Levett stated that Judge Swaine & he refused a similar application last year.

184. THE ELECTION OF 1864

"The True Issue or 'That's Whats the Matter'." Lithographic cartoon by Currier & Ives, New York, 1864.　　　P

In the State elections held in the fall of 1861 there appeared a Union Party ticket, representing a coalition of all men, regardless of party, who supported the war in the North. A national convention of this party, held at Baltimore in June 1864, nominated Abraham Lincoln for reelection as President. For the Vice Presidency, a Tennessee Democrat, Andrew Johnson, was named. The "Peace Democrats," who pronounced the war a failure and demanded the restoration of the Union by a negotiated peace, met in Chicago and nominated George B. McClellan. Under the slogan "The Union as it was. The Constitution as it is," McClellan appeared a formidable candidate until Union military successes assured Lincoln's reelection. This pro-McClellan cartoon shows Presidents Lincoln and Davis tearing apart a map of the United States; McClellan seeks to restrain them.

185. CAMPAIGNING FOR THE SOLDIER VOTE

"How Shall Soldiers Vote?" New York, [1864]. Broadside. From the Alfred Whital Stern Collection.   R

The vote of the soldiers was an important factor in the State and national elections of 1864. The administration party, especially, was anxious that soldiers be granted furloughs to vote at home. Some States, New York and Ohio for example, made arrangements for the soldiers to vote in the field. It has been conceded that without the soldiers' vote in 1864, which went overwhelmingly for Lincoln, he could not have been reelected. These elections, the first instances of absentee voting in the United States, were not held completely without confusion. A carefully worded suggestion to Gen. William T. Sherman from the President that Indiana soldiers who could be spared be allowed to go home to vote in the State elections was responded to with such zeal that one Vermont regiment, the 19th, found itself voting in the Indiana elections. This poster urges Union soldiers to vote Republican.

THE HOME FRONT

The war was, in President Lincoln's phrase, "a people's contest," a struggle between entire populations testing to the utmost their relative capacities to raise and supply the armies of their nations. Few persons were left untouched by the war and its effects, particularly in the Confederacy, where devastation, the blockade, inflation, and the collapse of the economic system produced great distress. Behind the lines, in both the North and the South, men and women worked earnestly, however they could, to make the lot of the soldier more comfortable and to advance the cause in which they believed.

186. THE CONFEDERATE TRANSPORTATION SYSTEM WEAKENS

Petition from a Convention of Railroad Presidents and Superintendents, held in Richmond on Friday, Dec. 6, 1861. Two-page manuscript document. From the Pickett Papers.   MSS

In the transportation of men and supplies, the Union began the war with a distinct advantage which increased rapidly throughout the war. The railroad system of the North was larger, better equipped, and more efficiently managed than that of the Confederacy. In addition to existing lines—placed, where necessary, under military control early in 1862—new tracks, bridges, and even entire railroads were constructed by Union army engineers. (Grant's siege of Petersburg was supported by a road built especially for the purpose.) In the Confederacy the lines were largely local in character, different track gauges often made connections impossible, and centralized authority for controlling the railroads for military purposes was lacking until the war was nearly over. In addition to these handicaps, the Confederate railroad system was seriously hampered by a lack of skilled labor and of supplies, especially nails, to repair lines and equipment as they deteriorated or were destroyed. Shown is a petition from a Convention of Virginia railroad men to President Jefferson Davis, urging that supplies be allocated for the repair of the railroads.

187. SHORTAGE OF METAL IN THE CONFEDERACY

"Offering of Bells to be Cast into Cannon." Etching no. 19 in Adalbert J. Volck's *Con-*

federate War Etchings ([Baltimore(?), 18—]). R

A dramatic gesture of the war, which pointed up the scarcity of essential raw materials within the Confederacy, was the offering of church bells to be melted down and cast into cannon. Although the net result of such sacrifices was probably negligible, they seem to have been repeated. The May 1, 1862, issue of *The Index*, the Pro-Confederate weekly published in London, carried a letter from Gen. P. G. T. Beauregard encouraging such gifts. Taken from the Mobile *Register* of March 18 and addressed to the "Planters of the Mississippi Valley," the letter reads:

> More than once a People fighting with an enemy less ruthless than yours . . . have not hesitated to melt and mould into cannon the precious bells surmounting their houses of God, which had called generations to prayer. . . .
>
> We want cannon as greatly as any people whoever, as history tells you, melted their church bells to supply them; and I, your general, . . . do now call on you to send your plantation bells to the nearest railroad depot subject to my order, to be melted into cannon for the defense of your plantations.
>
> Who will not cheerfully and promptly send me his bells under such circumstances?
>
> Be of good cheer; but time is precious.

188. THE LEADING ARSENAL OF THE CONFEDERACY

"The Tredegar Works, Richmond, Va." Colored lithograph by E. Sachse, Baltimore, 1865, after F. Dielman. P

This iron works, built in 1836, was, until 1863, the Confederacy's only source for heavy guns. During the war it produced nearly 1,100 cannon, and here the plates for the *Merrimack* were forged. Its importance made the defense of Richmond vital to the success of the Confederate States. Brilliantly managed by Joseph Reid Anderson, the Tredegar Works was almost self-sustaining. In addition to obtaining pig iron from hearth furnaces in the Virginia mountains, its agents combed the South to insure that the laborers were fed and clothed. In spite of difficulties

of transportation and supply, the works continued production until the fall of Richmond.

189. A CIVIL WAR "IDENTIFICATION CARD"

Pass to and from the Tredegar Iron Works, Richmond, 186-. Broadside form. From the Confederate Miscellany Collection. MSS

Mechanics and artisans were scarce in the Confederacy and the Tredegar Iron Works operated largely with skilled slave labor and, occasionally, with the help of prisoners who had taken the oath and been paroled. This pass, issued by the Works, permitted workers to be absent during the night.

190. ARMAMENTS IN THE NORTH

"The Ft. Pitt Works from the River, Pittsburgh, Pa." Photocopy of wood engraving in *Harper's Weekly*, Aug. 23, 1862, after Theodore R. Davis. P

The Union armies held a distinct advantage in being supported by superior production capacity. During the war approximately 4 million small arms and 7,800 cannon were issued to the Federal army, totals far larger than the comparable figures for the Confederacy which was forced to depend upon capture and foreign purchases to augment its smaller munitions industry. The Union, too, in the first year of the war was forced to purchase arms abroad, and its efforts led a neutral observer to comment that the "refuse of all Europe passed into the hands of the American volunteers." The production of arms within the Union increased dramatically, however, as existing government facilities were expanded. The United States arsenal at Springfield, Mass., for example was soon employing 2,800 workmen, exempt from the draft, and providing 20,000 muskets a month. Private manufacturers, often with great profit, turned to making guns and contributed heavily to the Union's supremacy in equipment. Shown is a wood engraving of a plant in Pittsburgh, which, in 1862, was producing 15- and 20-inch Rodman guns for "the *Roanoke*" and "the new *Monitors* and all our coast fortifications." This works, the West Point Foundry, and Alger's in Boston, were three of the largest wartime cannon foundries in the North.

191. CONFEDERATE POWDER WORKS, AUGUSTA, GA.

Photograph by unidentified photographer.
P

George W. Rains, in charge of Confederate gunpowder production during the war, recalled in 1882 that "the entire supply of gunpowder in the Confederacy at the beginning of the conflict, was scarcely sufficient for one month of active operations, and not a pound was being made throughout its limits. To enter upon a great war without a supply of this essential material, and without effective means of procuring it from abroad, or of manufacturing it at home, was appalling." Rains' remedy for the situation was the de-development of a powder manufactory at Augusta, Ga. This city was selected, Rains explained, "for its central position; for its canal transportation and water-power; for its railroad facilities; and for its security from attack." Powder mills were established elsewhere in the South, but the Augusta establishment was by far the largest in the Confederacy, producing 1,375 tons of gunpowder between April 10, 1862, and April 18, 1865.

192. HOW "KING COTTON" AFFECTED THE WAR

"Cottonburners in the Neighborhood of Memphis Surprised by Federal Scouts." Photocopy of wood engraving in *The Illustrated London News*, Aug. 9, 1862, after Frank Vizetelly.
P

In addition to the intricacies of the cotton embargo, whereby Confederate authorities hoped to force Great Britain into intervention by denying English textile mills the raw material they needed to operate, cotton was a factor of considerable complexity within both the Confederacy and the Union. Confederates followed the official policy of destroying cotton (as depicted), rather than let it fall into the hands of the advancing Federal armies. Cotton was not always burned, however. The restricted trade in the commodity, authorized by the Union early in the war (in those areas controlled by the army), expanded tremendously and illegally. Often both planter and buyer, eager for the immense profits involved, violated the laws of their nations; and Confederate cotton was exchanged for Yankee dollars or, sometimes, for supplies used to support the Southern armies. Ulysses S. Grant estimated that this illicit trade, in which at one time nearly $2 million worth of supplies passed through Memphis each month, prolonged the war a year.

193. THE PROBLEM OF WARTIME PROFITEERS

Two-page holograph letter from Henry W. Halleck to Montgomery C. Meigs, Jan. 22, 1862. From the Halleck Papers.
MSS

In the early years of the war an inefficient procurement system, under which the Federal Government and the individual States bid against each other for supplies, led to notorious contracts and shameful consequences. Unscrupulous contractors, often abetted by corrupt officials, furnished the armies, at inflated prices, with worthless foreign guns; substituted sand for sugar and paper for leather; sold spoiled food; and supplied tents and blankets which quickly disintegrated. Inferior clothing, known as "shoddy," was furnished to the soldiers, who had to pay for it themselves from their meager clothing allowance of $42 per year. Under the administration of Secretary of War Edwin M. Stanton, beginning in January 1862, a strenuous effort at reform was made, but throughout the war army contractors were somewhat suspect. In this letter Henry W. Halleck, commanding in

BRITISH ARTIST-CORRESPONDENT FRANK VIZETELLY. *Photograph by Mathew B. Brady, 1861 or 1862.*
(See entry 151.)

War Department,
July 20, 1861.

Mr R. Young
and give such
you to General
McDowell's
Encampment on
business con-
nected with
this department.

Simon Cameron
Secy of War

A WAR CORRESPONDENT WHO BECAME LIBRARIAN OF CONGRESS. *Single-page holograph pass for John R. Young, July 20, 1861, signed by Simon Cameron.* (*See entry 156.*)

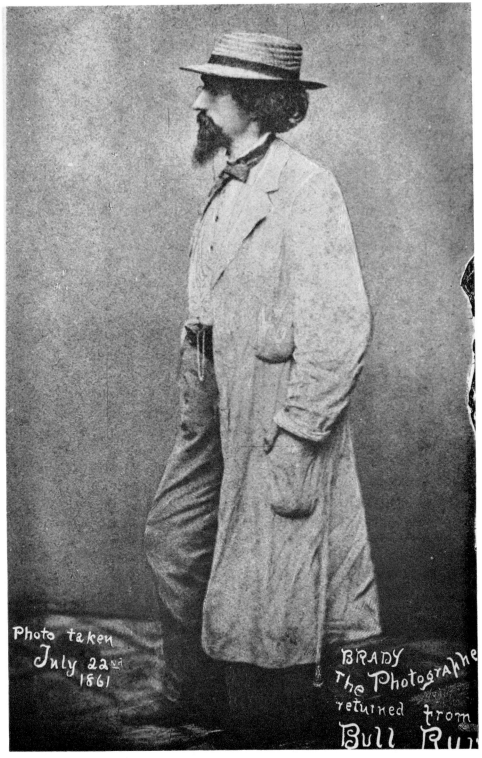

Photo taken
July 22ⁿᵈ
1861

BRADY
The Photographe[r]
returned from
Bull Ru[n]

MATHEW B. BRADY, WARTIME PHOTOGRAPHER IN THE NORTH.   *Photograph by unidentified photographer,*
July 1861.   (See entry 159.)

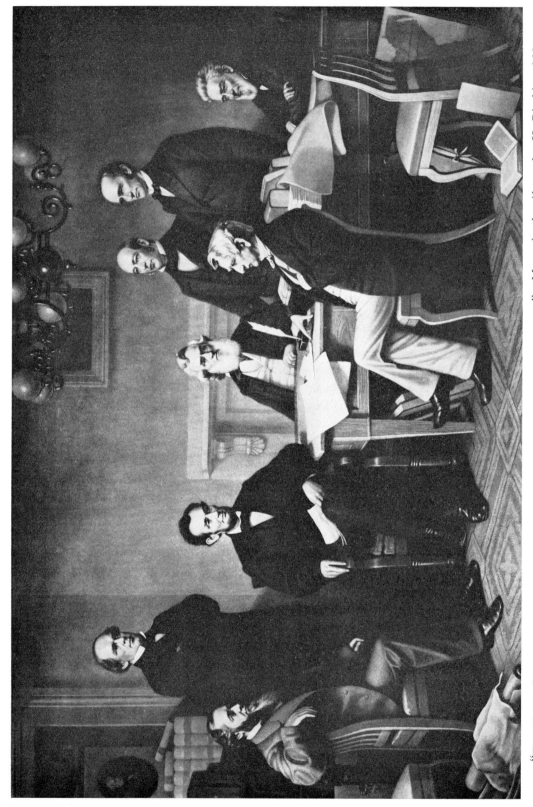

"THE FIRST READING OF THE EMANCIPATION PROCLAMATION BEFORE THE CABINET."   *Mezzotint by Alexander H. Ritchie, 1866.*

(See entry 163.)

"JEFFERSON DAVIS AND HIS CABINET, WITH GENERAL LEE." *Lithograph by Thomas Kelly, New York, 1866.* (*See entry 165.*)

"THE SEIZURE BY CAPTAIN WILKS [*sic*], OF THE UNITED STATES' WAR-SHIP *San Jacinto*, OF MESSRS. SLIDELL AND MASON, CONFEDERATE COMMISSIONERS, ON BOARD THE BRITISH MAIL-STEAMER *Trent*." *Wood engraving in* The Illustrated London News, *Dec. 7, 1861.* (*See entry 172.*)

"NOT ANY, WE THANK YOU MR. DAVIS." *Lithographic cartoon by Ehrgott, Forbriger & Co., 1861.* (*See entry 175.*)

"READING THE EMANCIPATION PROCLAMATION." *Engraving by J. W. Watts, 1864.* (*See entry 178.*)

"BUILDINGS OF THE GREAT CENTRAL FAIR, IN AID OF THE U.S. SANITARY COMMISSION, LOGAN SQUARE, PHILADELPHIA, JUNE 1864." *Colored lithograph by P. S. Duval & Son, Philadelphia. (See entry 194.)*

"UNION VOLUNTEER REFRESHMENT SALOON OF PHILADELPHIA." Colored lithograph by T. Sinclair, Philadelphia. (See entry 196.)

"THE RIOTS IN NEW YORK: THE MOB BURNING THE PROVOST MARSHALL'S OFFICE." *Wood engraving in* The Illustrated London News, *Aug. 8, 1863. (See entry 199.)*

"THE UNION A B C." *Boston,* [*1864*]. (*See entry 202.*)

"MAKING CLOTHES FOR THE BOYS IN THE ARMY." *Etching no. 11 in Adalbert J. Volck's Confederate War Etchings ([Baltimore(?), 18—]).*

(See entry 208.)

"THE PALMETTO STATE SONG." *Sheet music. Charleston, S.C., [1861?]. (See entry 209.)*

"THE DRUMMER BOY OF SHILOH." *Sheet music. Louisville and Chicago, [1863]. (See entry 221.)*

"O IM A GOOD OLD REBEL." *Sheet music [n.p., 186–] (see entry 226.)*

the West, complains to Quartermaster-General Montgomery C. Meigs about the inferior clothing issued his troops:

The issue of inferior clothing & blankets may have been a necessity. The great complaint is about the prices. It is said that a pair of these inferior pantaloons will not last two weeks; yet the full price must be charged. The extra clothing issued to some regiments in the field amounts to more than their pay. This creates great dissatisfaction. The clothing now received is good; but the cloth sent here from Philadelphia to be made up is said to be worthless. Can't deductions be made on former issues of inferior articles? It would do much to satisfy the men.

There is a strong feeling in the West against the authorities on account of inferior clothing & arms. Politicians are seeking to divert this dissatisfaction to sinister purposes.

194. THE "SANITARY FAIRS" OF 1863 AND 1864

"Buildings of the Great Central Fair, in Aid of the U.S. Sanitary Commission, Logan Square, Philadelphia, June 1864." Colored lithograph by P. S. Duval & Son, Philadelphia, after James Queen. (*See illustration.*) P

The United States Sanitary Commission was created in June 1861 for the purpose of caring for the sick and wounded of the Federal army and their dependents. The Commission, headed by the Reverend H. W. Bellows, augmented and inspected medical facilities, provided hospital trains and steamers, maintained eating facilities for transient troops, and greatly improved the lot of the soldier in camp. Funds for its work came from private contributions, from churches, and especially from "Sanitary fairs." The first of these elaborate fairs, intended to raise money by admissions and the sale of objects (including a manuscript of the Emancipation Proclamation in Lincoln's hand), was held in Chicago late in 1863. In the following months nearly every large city in the North, including Philadelphia, held such fairs.

195. CITIZENS' VOLUNTEER SERVICES IN "THE CITY OF BROTHERLY LOVE"

"To the Patriotic Women of Philadelphia." Philadelphia, [1861]. Broadside. R

Their achievements as nurses (*see* entry 143) or spies brought considerable fame to certain women, North and South, but the majority of the women in the war served anonymously. Some aided by working in factories. Others worked directly with the soldiers, usually without reward or recognition, to make their lot a happier one. This broadside poster, printed early in the war and signed "Many Ladies," calls on "the patriotic women of Philadelphia" to meet "to devise means to give aid and comfort to our noble soldiers."

196. A CIVIL WAR U.S.O.

"Union Volunteer Refreshment Saloon of Philadelphia, Being the First Institution of the Kind in the United States. Organized May 27th 1861." Colored lithograph by T. Sinclair, Philadelphia, after J. Queen (*See illustration.*) P

The Union Volunteer Refreshment Saloon was one of two truly great institutions in Philadelphia (the other was the Cooper Shop Volunteer Refreshment Saloon) which ministered to the needs and saw to the comforts of Federal troops en route to and from the battlefields of the war. Its location, as the lithograph shows, on the southwest corner of Washington and Swanson Streets, beside the Navy Yard, rendered it easily accessible by boat or by the trains of the Philadelphia, Wilmington & Baltimore Rail Road Company. Sustained entirely by voluntary contributions from the citizens of Philadelphia and vicinity, it provided the soldier with facilities for bathing, writing letters, entertainment, and temporary quarters. It also had two hospitals (one is depicted), with a combined capacity of 100 beds. Two years after its organization on May 27, 1861 (and with it the arrival at 3 a.m. the next morning of the 8th New York Regiment, with 800 men), the Union Volunteer Refreshment Committee could boast that nearly 300,000 men had been "received, entertained, and provided for" in that time and could exult in a letter of May 15, 1862, from Lincoln, in which the President wrote: "if they [the Union Volunteer Refreshment Saloon and the Cooper Shop] have dealt so generously with our Volunteers, as I have frequently heard, and believe, they are indeed worthy of all praise."

197. "CLOSE UP" OF THE UNION VOLUNTEER REFRESHMENT SALOON

"Volunteer Refreshment Saloon, Supported Gratuitously By the Citizens, of Philadelphia, Pa." Lithograph by W. Boell, Philadelphia, 1861.   P

Shown is the main building, formerly a boat shop and riggers' loft, together with interior views of the men's "Washing Department," the "Cooking Department," and the "Dining Saloon," which could seat at the tables 1,200 at one time. Depicted also is a 5-car train of the Philadelphia, Wilmington & Baltimore Rail Road Company, preparing to depart.

198. A SOLDIERS' AID SOCIETY

"U.S. Christian Commission, Meal Ticket." [Peoria(?), Ill., 186–] Printed card. From the George H. Stuart Papers.   MSS

Various societies, both Union and Confederate, were organized for the welfare of the soldiers. The United States Christian Commission, established by the Y.M.C.A. to attend to the spiritual welfare of the Union armies, was similar in organization to the United States Sanitary Commission. It provided the Union armies with writing materials, reading rooms, and reading matter, gave assistance to transient soldiers, and ar-

ranged for religious services. The meal ticket displayed, issued by the Commission, was "good for one meal" at any of 14 U.S.C.C. stations in Illinois.

199. THE DRAFT RIOTS IN NEW YORK CITY

"The Riots in New York: the Mob Burning the Provost Marshall's Office." Photocopy of wood engraving in *The Illustrated London News*, Aug. 8, 1863. (*See illustration.*) P

The draft established by the Act of March 3, 1863, brought disturbances in Rutland, Vt.; Wooster, Ohio; Portsmouth, N.H.; Boston; and, especially, in New York City. Here a riot produced nearly 1,000 casualties and caused great loss of property. The drawing of lots began on July 11, 1863, at the Ninth Congressional District draft headquarters. Two days later a mob, mostly foreign-born laborers, attacked the building, overcame police and firemen, and for 4 days terrorized the city, burning government buildings, hotels, and residences of prominent Republicans. On the return of military regiments, which had earlier been sent toward Gettysburg, order was restored. On August 19, guarded by troops from the Army of the Potomac, the drawings were peaceably resumed. The principal resentment of the draft and the immediate cause of the riot was the substitution clause, whereby money could be given instead of service.

200. CIVILIAN HARDSHIP AT VICKSBURG

"The Civil War in America. Southern Refugees Encamping in the Woods near Vicksburg." Photocopy of wood engraving in *The Illustrated London News*, Aug. 29, 1863, after Frank Vizetelly.   P

The war was fought almost entirely in the Confederacy, and very often civilians of the Southern States were directly affected by it. This was especially true of the citizens of

Vicksburg in 1863. Besieged, together with Pemberton's Confederate army, from May 22 until July 4, they lived in caves or in wooded areas outside the city to escape the daily bombardments of the city. To the encampment of women and children, in the illustration, a cavalry soldier has evidently just brought the mail.

201. TEXTBOOKS FOR SOUTHERN CHILDREN

The Confederate Primer. 4th ed. Richmond, 1864.   R

In Confederate schools the need was soon felt for textbooks which would popularize and defend the institutions of the South. Dependent at first upon the North, Confederate teachers and writers soon produced a flood of primers, readers, grammars, geographies, arithmetics, spellers, and other books, in some instances Northern texts which had been "revised and improved, and adapted to the use of schools in the Confederate States."

One of the first books to appear was *The First Confederate Speller,* written by "an association of southern teachers" and published in Nashville in 1861. Others followed rapidly, including Mrs. Marinda B. Moore's delightful series: *The Dixie Primer, for the Little Folks* (1862); *The First Dixie Reader; Designed to Follow the Dixie Primer* (1863); *The Dixie Speller, to Follow the First Dixie Reader* (1864); and *The Geographical Reader, for the Dixie Children* (1863). These were published in Raleigh, N.C.

In some texts problems were phrased or words defined so as to demean the North and glorify the South. L. Johnson's *An Elementary Arithmetic* (1864) poses this problem for beginners: "7 Confederate soldiers captured 21 Yankees and divided them equally among them; how many did each one have?"

The little booklet displayed, its covers printed on wallpaper, is one of several published in Richmond by George L. Bidgood

and written, according to the publisher, by Prof. Richard M. Smith of Randolph-Macon College. Other titles are *The Confederate First Reader* and *The Confederate Spelling Book.*

202. BOOKS FOR "YANKEE" CHILDREN

The Union A B C. Boston, [1864]. (*See illustration.*)   R

Northern publishers of school texts, not to be outdone by those of the South, turned out patriotic titles of their own, as exemplified by such books of 1864 as *The United States Primer* (its cover bears a flag, shield, and the label "Union"), published in New York by the American Tract Society, and *The Union A B C.* The latter represents the letters of the alphabet with key words and appropriate illustrations drawn, for childish edification, from such timely subjects as: Civil War soldiers ("Z is Zouave, who charged on the foe"), armament ("G is a Gun, that is used in the war"), heroic figures ("D is a Drummer Boy, called little Ben"), patriotic symbols ("F is our Flag, that shall wave evermore"), and other topics at this time uppermost in people's minds (*e.g.,* "W is for War, which we all of us rue"). The booklet, two letters of the alphabet to a page, is printed on linen with engraved illustrations (after "Dyer") of red and blue on white.

203. MEETING THE PROBLEM OF FOOD FOR THE ARMIES OF THE SOUTH

Two-page handwritten letter from Jefferson Davis to Joseph E. Brown, Jan. 27, 1863. Signed by Davis. From the Davis Papers.   MSS

Southern planters, as the war progressed, were urged to limit the production of the traditional cash crops (cotton and tobacco) and increase the production of provisions for the army. This is a letter on the subject from President Davis to one of his severest critics,

Governor Brown of Georgia. The problem of provisions, never solved, stemmed in part from an inadequate transportation system which could not deliver the food, raised in abundance in parts of Georgia and Alabama, to Lee's starving army in Virginia. Aware of the gravity of the situation, Davis writes:

I have received and read with interest your letter enclosing a copy of an Act and Joint Resolution of the Legislature of Georgia, partially prohibiting the cultivation of cotton in the State during the continuance of the war, and urging upon planters the necessity for increased attention to the production of provisions.

The inauguration of this policy affords me great gratification . . . From the general adaption of the scheme we may anticipate the best results.

The possibility of a short supply of provisions presents the greatest danger to a successful prosecution of the war. If we shall be able to furnish adequate subsistence to the army during the coming season, we may set at defiance the worst efforts of our enemy. A general compliance by the farmers and planters, therefore, with the suggestions of this Joint Resolution will be the guarantee of our independence.

204. CONFEDERATES "ON RELIEF"

Going to the Commissary for Rations. Rappahannock Station, Va., Feb. 18, 1864. Pencil drawing by Edwin Forbes.   P

The Union armies devastated the areas they marched through, stripping them bare of provisions, and the destitute civilians in their wake were often dependent upon the Federal government for food. This was especially true during the winter months. The drawing depicts Southern women en route to a commissary for food.

205. INFLATION IN THE CONFEDERACY

Single-page holograph letter from Andrew Ewing to Henry Watterson, Feb. 17, 1864. From the Watterson Papers.   MSS

In the closing years of the war, with the Confederate economy disrupted by the effects of the blockade and the ravages of marching armies, prices reached fantastic heights. In Richmond in 1864 corn meal, for example, sold for $50 a bushel, potatoes for $30 and beans for $75. In this letter Henry Watterson, who later gained great journalistic fame, is asked by a friend for one of the scarcest of all commodities, coffee:

Col. Worthington arrived on yesterday and said you would be up to see us in a few days and wished to know whether we wanted coffee. We have decided to buy five pounds which please buy and bring with you and also a good horse brush & currycomb or either if they can be procured and my boots. I send you a check for one hundred dollars. You had better have them all put up in one package and keep your eye on it. . . .

206. A BOOK OF RECIPES "ADAPTED TO THE TIMES"

Confederate Receipt Book. A Compilation of Over One Hundred Receipts, Adapted to the Times. Richmond, 1863.   R

Cessation of trade with the North, the demands of war, and the blockade of its ports, deprived the South of most of the luxuries and many of the essentials of everyday life. There were shortages, especially, in drugs and medicines and in certain foods. During the early years of the war, substitutes for these were sought and, when found, whether by chance or through experiment, they were passed on—either orally, through written notes, or by publication in the newspapers. Based upon these and other sources, there appeared in 1863 two publications. One, written at the request of the Surgeon General, was Francis P. Porcher's *Resources of the Southern Fields and Forests,* a serious and extensive study of new and substitute medicines to be derived from the flora of the South. The other is this little compilation of recipes, a curiosity today but no doubt of great practical value at the time. It includes not only recipes for "apple pie without apples" and "artificial oysters," remedies for certain minor afflictions, and a formula for "charcoal tooth powder"; but, above all, a "substitute for coffee":

Take sound ripe acorns, wash them while in the shell, dry them, and parch until they open, take the shell off, roast with a little bacon fat, and you will have a splendid cup of coffee.

207. ANOTHER MEANS OF SUPPLY

"Smuggling Medicines into the South." Etching no. 18 in Adalbert J. Volck's *Confederate War Etchings* ([Baltimore(?), 18—]).   R

Early in the war a relatively easy system of crossing into enemy territory was established. Spies crossed the Potomac into both nations, sometimes carrying letters (at $1.50 each). Contraband of war, especially quinine and morphine, was smuggled into the Confederacy, women, with their voluminous petticoats and hoop skirts, being especially adept at getting such medicines through the lines. The smugglers in this etching, who are evidently behind Union lines (a lookout is posted in a tree), are transferring medicine from a boat to a horse.

208. HOW THE SOUTH CLOTHED HER SOLDIERS

"Making Clothes for the Boys in the Army." Etching no. 11 in Adalbert J. Volck's *Confederate War Etchings* ([Baltimore(?), 18—]). (*See illustration.*)   R

A Texan in 1864 wrote from near Atlanta that "In this army, one hole in the seat of the breeches indicates a captain, two holes a lieutenant, and the seat of the pants all out indicates that the individual is a private." Sometimes barefooted and lacking blankets and coats (which they invariably discarded on a march, as did their Union counterparts), Confederate soldiers came to rely upon their own resources to complete their uniforms, which sometimes included "Yankee" pants, shoes, and even coats. Soldiers' aid societies and the women of their families also came to be important sources of supply. From the "homespun" cloth produced by spinning wheels and hand looms (depicted

in the etching), Confederate women fashioned clothing to supplement the inadequate issues from the government. From Thomas County, Ga., for example, Mrs. Moses Linton sent a Maryland regiment two boxes containing "168 pr. pants, 76 jackits [*sic*], 8 pr. socks, 1 pr. pillows, 6 shirts, 6 towels, 6 pillow cases."

THE SONGS OF THE WAR

No other American war nor any other event in our history produced the amount and quality of music inspired by the Civil War. The majority of the thousands of songs published during the conflict have been forgotten, but some survived both the war and the intervening years to become an integral part of our musical heritage. Those which were most popular were those which accurately reflected the mood of people undergoing a great emotional experience. In general, the best of the patriotic songs appeared early in the war. Thereafter, as a sentimental and ingenuous generation came to know the realities of war, songs of sorrow and unabashed sentimentality became the favorites. The most popular of these knew no national boundaries and were sung, and often published, in both the Union and the Confederacy.

209. THE FIRST MUSIC OF THE CONFEDERACY

The Palmetto State Song. Music composed and respectfully dedicated to the signers of the ordinance of secession unanimously passed in convention at Charleston, S.C.,

Dec'r 20th 1860, by Geo. O. Robinson. Charleston, S.C., [1861?]. (*See illustration.*) MUS

Inspired by the secession ordinance of South Carolina on December 20, 1860, this song is possibly the earliest piece of sheet music published in the Confederacy. The cover, lithographed by A. Hoen & Co., Baltimore, after a drawing by A. Grinevald, shows the delegates to the Convention signing the ordinance in Institute Hall in Charleston. It is believed to be the only illustration of the scene.

210. THE FIRST SONG OF THE WAR

"The First Gun is Fired. 'May God Protect the Right.' Rallying song and chorus, by Geo. F. Root." Chicago, 1861. Broadside. MUS

On April 18, less than a week after the surrender of Fort Sumter, the first Union song of the war was copyrighted. Written by George Frederick Root of Chicago, an ardent abolitionist who became the most prominent songwriter of the war, the lyrics were typical of the stilted invective and defiance which characterized the early songs of the war:

The first gun is fired!
May God protect the right!
Let the free-born sons of the North arise
In power's avenging might!
Shall the glorious Union our fathers made,
By ruthless hands be sunder'd?
And we of freedom's sacred rights
By trait'rous foes be plunder'd?

211. SONGS POPULAR EARLY IN THE WAR.

(1) "War Songs." Pencil drawing by Winslow Homer; (2) "The Songs of the War." Photocopy of wood engraving in *Harper's Weekly*, Nov. 23, 1861, after Winslow Homer. P

This drawing, the only known Homer original in the Library of Congress, is indicative of what songs were regarded (by Homer at

least) as soldiers' favorites at the start of the war. The titles which appear in the drawing (actually a series of 8 small drawings or vignettes), with appropriately symbolic scenes, are: "Glory Hallelujah," "The Girl I Left Behind Me," "Hail to the Chief," "The Bold Soldier Boy," "We'll be Free and Easy Still," "Rogues March," "Reveille," and "Dixie." The final vignette ("Dixie") is untitled in the original drawing and differs in detail from the engraving based upon it which was published in *Harper's Weekly.* Even without the evidence of *Harper's*, the drawing, which is undated, has every appearance of belonging to the first year of the war. The title "Battle Hymn of the Republic" has not yet supplanted that of its precursor, "Glory Hallelujah" (*see* entry 213); and songs so characteristic of the final years of the war, less exuberant and more expressive of feelings of sorrow, homesickness, war-weariness, and the like, do not appear.

212. "IN DIXIE'S LAND"

I Wish I Was in Dixie's Land. Written & Composed expressly for Bryant's Minstrels by Dan D. Emmett. Arranged for the piano forte by W. L. Hobbs. New York, 1860. MUS

In New York City in 1859 Daniel Decatur Emmett produced what was to become the national song of the Confederacy. "Dixie," indelibly associated with the South, has since become known and loved throughout the world.

At the time Emmett was a composer and a member of Bryant's Minstrels. He wrote the song in compliance with a request from the manager of the troupe for "a new walk-around . . . something in the git-up and git style." In Emmett's words: "The next day, Sunday, was a very rainy day. I was in a gloomy mood. . . . All I could think of of was the good old circus days in the South. Finally I said right out loud, 'I wish I was in Dixie'. . . . in less than an hour I had the first verse and chorus."

Published as "In Dixie's Land," the song gained great popularity and became a standard number with minstrel troupes. It was used in the political campaign of 1860 and was, perhaps ironically, Abraham Lincoln's favorite. Its popularity in the South seems to have begun with its performance by Mrs. John Wood in a New Orleans performance of "Pochahanas Daughter" a few months before the war. It was played by Herman Arnold at the inauguration of Jefferson Davis in Montgomery, Ala., and was adopted as the favorite marching song of Confederate soldiers. Because of its lowly origins and homely phrases, "Dixie" was never completely accepted by the officials of the Confederacy, who regarded it as inappropriate as a national anthem. Several more dignified sets of words were adapted to the music, notably those by Albert Pike and John Hill Hewitt, but none of the parodies attained the popularity of the original. Emmett, a descendant of abolitionists and strongly pro-Union in his sentiments was widely denounced in the North for his great, but accidental contribution to the Confederacy.

213. THE ANTHEM OF THE UNION

Battle Hymn of the Republic. Adapted to the favorite melody of "Glory hallelujah," written by Mrs. Dr. S. G. Howe, for the *Atlantic Monthly*. Boston, 1862.   MUS

The most stately and stirring of all Union songs had its origins in the Deep South. The melody of "The Battle Hymn of the Republic" appeared sometime before 1855 as "Say Brother Will You Meet Us On Canaan's Happy Shore." A composition of William Steffe, described as both a native of Richmond and a South Carolinian, this song was widely sung at camp meetings in Georgia and South Carolina. The transition of this song into a marching song is not completely clear, but it is certain that in 1861 Federal soldiers were singing it with a new set of words—"John Brown's body lies

a-mouldering in the grave." This version, entitled "Glory Hallelujah!" was published in the same year. The parody has been traced to both the 2nd United States Infantry and the 12th Massachusetts Volunteers. Originally, it is said, the song was intended to taunt a sergeant named John Brown and not to celebrate the abolitionist hanged at Harper's Ferry. On November 21, 1861, Mrs. Julia Ward Howe, who with her husband edited the anti-slavery Boston *Commonwealth*, attended a review of troops held near Washington. Hearing the marching soldiers singing the song, her escort, the Reverend James Freeman Clarke, is alleged to have asked Mrs. Howe why she did not compose more fitting words to the stirring music. That night in her room at Willard's Hotel she wrote the great verses beginning, "Mine eyes have seen the glory of the coming of the Lord." The poem, for which she received $4, was first published in the *Atlantic* for February 1862 and appeared in music form in April.

214. THE WAR SONG OF THE UNION

The Battle Cry of Freedom. By Geo. F. Root. Chicago, 1863.   MUS

The greatest of the rallying songs of the war was introduced in Chicago in July 1862 by the Lumbard Brothers, a popular singing group. Presented in the East by the singing Hutchinson Family, "The Battle Cry of Freedom" was George F. Root's most popular and significant contribution. Root composed verses appropriate for both civilians and soldiers, and his song was invariably heard at public concerts and rallies as well as in the army camps. A Confederate version was issued by Hermann L. Schreiner with the chorus beginning: "Our Dixie forever, she's never at a loss." Dozens of anecdotes, some probably apochryphal, attest to the inspirational effect of the song with its combined themes of Union and freedom. One of the most persistent describes the men of a

Union army corps moving into the Battle of the Wilderness singing:

The Union forever, hurrah! boys, hurrah!
Down with the traitor and up with the star;
While we rally 'round the flag, boys, rally once
    again,
Shouting the battle-cry of freedom.

215. ONE OF THE WAR'S GREAT MARCHING SONGS

Maryland! My Maryland. Written by a Baltimorean in Louisiana. Music adapted & arranged by C. E. Baltimore, 1861. MUS

On April 19, 1861, the 6th Massachusetts Regiment, hurrying to the defense of Washington, clashed with a Confederate mob on the streets of Baltimore. Four days later James Ryder Randall, a 22-year-old teacher at Poydras College near New Orleans, wrote the verses which resulted in one of the great marching songs of the war and is still one of the best-known and most stirring of all State songs. Randall, a native of Baltimore and a man of strong secession sentiments, read his poem, "My Maryland," to his students. Upon their urging, he submitted it for publication in the New Orleans *Delta*. It appeared there on April 26 and was widely reprinted throughout the South. In Baltimore, where the poem gained a quick and wide popularity, the words were set to the music of "Lauriger Horatius" (better known as the German folk-air "Tannenbaum O Tannenbaum"). Credit for setting the verses to music is sometimes given to Jenny and Hetty Cary, whose other contributions to the Confederacy included gowns from which the first battle flag was made. Many years later Randall recalled that the Cary sisters sang the song to Virginia troops on July 4, 1861. There is some evidence that Miss Rebecca Lloyd Nicholson (a descendant of Joseph Hopper Nicholson, associated with the publication of "The Star Spangled Banner") first set Randall's verses to music. The great popularity of the song inspired a Union version. Entitled "Answer to My Maryland," this was an early example of the rather common practice of adapting popular songs to fit regional sentiments. This parodying led to Confederate lyrics for such Union favorites as "Yankee Doodle," "The Star Spangled Banner," "The Battle Cry of Freedom," and a Union version of "Dixie."

216. AN EARLY CONFEDERATE RALLYING SONG

The Song of the South. Composed & Respectfully dedicated to the Sons of the South by James H. Huber. Louisville, Ky., 1861.
        MUS

James H. Huber of Kentucky and Lena Lyle of Tennessee collaborated to produce one of the earliest of the patriotic songs of the Confederacy. The sentiment of the lyrics, that the Confederate soldier would conquer or die, was repeated often in songs produced in the enthusiasm of 1861. The Northern counterpart to this was an avowal of swift and terrible retribution.

The cover, lithographed by Hart & Mapother, Louisville, Ky., shows the "Flag as it is," with seven stars representing the original seceding States; and the "Flag as it will be," with eight additional stars added for the slave States still within the Union.

217. A CONFEDERATE FAVORITE

The Soldier's Suit of Grey. Words by Carrie B. Sinclair. Music by E. Clarke Ilsley. Augusta, Ga., [1864]. MUS

Carrie Belle Sinclair, reportedly a literary protégé of Alexander H. Stephens, Vice President of the Confederacy, collaborated with E. Clarke Ilsley to compose this Southern favorite, published by A. E. Blackmar, the leading music publisher of the South, who had been forced to move from New Orleans after Benjamin F. Butler had seized and destroyed his entire stock. The deterioration of the quality of Confederate paper and printing is evident in this publication.

64

218. THE SECOND SONG OF THE CONFEDERACY

The Bonnie Blue Flag. Composed, arranged, and sung at his personation concerts by Harry Macarthy, the Arkansas comedian. New Orleans, 1861.   MUS

The best of the Confederate songs appeared in 1861. Among these early ones, probably second only to "Dixie" in its popularity, was "The Bonnie Blue Flag." The title refers to the banner used by South Carolina for a short period following its secession, and the music is that of "The Irish Jaunting Car." Harry B. Macarthy, a professional entertainer, composed it and appears to have performed it on his programs in Jackson, Miss., in the spring of 1861; but it is generally agreed that the song gained its greatest acceptance during the following September, when it was sung in New Orleans in the Varieties Theater. Its popularity continued throughout the war; and, during the occupation of New Orleans, Gen. Benjamin F. Butler is said to have arrested Armaund E. Blackmar for ignoring an official order to discontinue its publication. "The Bonnie Blue Flag" was parodied several times. "Reply to the Bonnie Blue Flag" (a Northern version) and "The Home Spun Dress" (a Confederate composition) were among the most successful.

219. AN INCIDENT OF THE WAR IN SONG

All Quiet Along the Potomac To-Night. Words by Lamar Fontaine. Music by J. H. Hewitt. Columbia, S.C., and Richmond, Va., [186–].   MUS

"All Quiet Along the Potomac" (known also as "The Picket Guard") was a widely favored sentimental song. The authorship of the lyrics has been claimed by both Lamar Fontaine, a Confederate major, and Mrs. Ethel Lynn Beers of Goshen, N.Y. The title is derived from an announcement made frequently by the War Department in the fall of 1861: "All Quiet Along the Potomac." This was followed in one instance by "A picket was shot." A poem by Mrs. Beers, based upon this incident and entitled "The Picket Guard," appeared in *Harper's Weekly* on November 30, 1861, and was quickly set to music by several composers. In the South, where the song became immensely popular, the music was supplied by John H. Hewitt, the leading Confederate composer. This is the Southern version, dedicated "To the Unknown Dead of the Present Revolution."

220. "THREE HUNDRED THOUSAND MORE"

We Are Coming, Father Abraham, 300,000 More. Music arranged by J. A. Getze. Philadelphia, [1862].   MUS

On July 1, 1862, Abraham Lincoln issued a proclamation calling for 300,000 volunteers to serve for 3 years. James Sloan Gibbons of New York City responded with verses which became a great rallying cry for the Union. Gibbons, a successful banker, a Quaker, and an active abolitionist, was inspired to write:

We are coming, Father Abr'am,
Three hundred thousand more,
From Mississippi's winding stream
And from New England's shore.

The poem was published in the New York *Evening Post* on July 12 and was so widely attributed to the editor of that paper, William Cullen Bryant, that he was forced to make a public disavowal of authorship. The words were quickly set to music by several composers, including Stephen Collins Foster, but the most popular version was probably that by L. O. Emerson. The most dramatic performance of the song, according to one account, was at Grover's Theater in Washington. Here "Tad" Lincoln, the President's son, left his father's side to reappear later on stage, dressed in patriotic costume, where he led the ensemble and audience in singing the song.

221. A FREQUENT SENTIMENTAL SUBJECT

The Drummer Boy of Shiloh. A beautiful ballad written & composed by Will. S. Hays. Louisville and Chicago, [1863]. (*See illustration.*) MUS

The drummer boy dead on the field of battle was a theme which appealed strongly to the sentimentality of the age. Writers and publishers exploited this appeal with a series of songs: "The Dying Drummer," "The Dying Drummer Boy," "The Drummer Boy of Antietam," and "The Drummer Boy of Vicksburg." The first of the type to appear, "The Drummer Boy of Shiloh," was written by William Shakespeare Hays, a clerk in a Louisville, Ky., music store, and was published in the Union as well as in the Confederacy. In the latter it was dedicated to Harry B. Macarthy, writer of "The Bonnie Blue Flag."

222. THE VETERANS' FAVORITE

Tenting on the Old Camp Ground. Words & Music by Walter Kittredge, Adapted & sung by the Hutchinson Family. Boston, 1864. MUS

The war-weariness of the North was reflected in this song, published in 1864. Walter Kittredge of New Hampshire composed it in 1862, after he had received his draft notice. Ironically, he was rejected for physical disability. Attempting to sell the song, Kittredge met with little encouragement from publishers, who were then interested in more martial music. He had, however, once sung with one of the several companies of the Hutchinson Family Singers, and Asa Hutchinson agreed to perform the song at a concert near Lynn, Mass. After this performance the success of the song was assured. A publisher was easily found, and Kittredge and Hutchinson divided the royalties, greater than those Hutchinson ever received from any other song. It became popular with

Confederate soldiers, although it was never issued by a Southern publisher. The melancholy of the song was sometimes heightened by ending the final chorus with: "Dying tonight, Dying tonight, Dying on the old camp ground."

223. THE SOLDIER'S FAREWELL

The Girl I Left Behind Me. Arranged by J. C. Viereck. Macon and Savannah, [186–?]. MUS

Among the songs most popular with the soldiers were several written long before the war. "Home, Sweet Home" was a favorite of the troops, as were "Annie Laurie," "Listen to the Mocking-Bird," and the traditional song of leave-taking exhibited. The lilting melody of "The Girl I Left Behind Me" came to the United States from Ireland and became a universal favorite. A dialect parody, "I Goes to Fight Mit Sigel," was popular in the North, where large numbers of German-born served in the Union ranks.

224. A FORGOTTEN FAVORITE

Lorena. Written by Rev. H. D. L. Webster. Music by J. P. Webster. Macon, Ga. [186–?]. MUS

In September 1864 the Confederate army evacuated Atlanta, singing, as it marched, "Lorena," perhaps the most widely sung of all Civil War musical compositions. It first appeared in 1857, with lyrics by a Zanesville, Ohio, minister, Henry D. Webster, who, it is said, based his poem upon his unsuccessful courtship of one Ella Blocksom, who married instead a future Chief Justice of Ohio. The beautiful melody was furnished by a professional, Joseph P. Webster (his relationship with the lyricist is disputed), a native of New Hampshire who had migrated to Wisconsin. Despite its Northern origin, "Lorena" attained its greatest popularity in the South, where babies and even a steamboat were named for the heroine of the song. Shown is a publication of this great favorite by a Macon, Ga., firm, John C. Schreiner and Son, who became publishers after the war had begun, using a font of music type smuggled through the Federal lines from Philadelphia, via Cincinnati, Louisville, and Nashville.

225. LONGING FOR HOME

The Soldier's Vision. Music and Words by C. Everest. Philadelphia, [1862]. MUS

This is one example of the dozens of songs published during the war which concerned themselves with the soldier's yearnings for family, old friends, and home. The attractively illustrated cover was lithographed by T. Sinclair of Philadelphia.

226. AN UNRECONSTRUCTED REBEL

O Im a Good Old Rebel. By I. R. [n.p., 186–]. (*See illustration.*) MUS

The last of the songs with a Confederate point of view appeared shortly after the war, probably in 1866. "O, I'm a Good Old Rebel" was a comic song which expressed in backwoods dialect the justified resentment of many Southerners of the reconstruction being forced upon them. The lyrics, concluding with the line "I don't want no pardon for anything I done," have been attributed to Maj. Innes Randolph. The song was "Respectfully dedicated to the Hon. Thad[deus] Stevens," a Pennsylvania Congressman and one of the leaders of the group advocating a harsh reconstruction policy.

227. SONGS THE CONSCRIPTS SANG

Grafted into the Army. Words & music by Henry C. Work. Chicago, 1862. MUS

Throughout the solemn years of war, comic songs enjoyed a considerable popularity with both soldiers and civilians. Confederates found humor in "Short Rations: Or the Corn-Fed Army of Tennessee," and "Here's Your Mule," a meaningless expression similar to "Where's Elmer?" and "Kilroy Was Here," of World Wars I and II. Conscription in the Union produced such songs as "Where are You, $300?," "How Are You Exempt?," and "Wanted: A Substitute," each title referring to a means of evading service. Probably the most popular of the songs which lampooned the Federal draft was Henry C. Work's "Grafted Into the Army." The verse begins:

Our Jimmy has gone for to live in a tent,
They have grafted him into the army.
He finally puckered up courage and went,
When they grafted him into the army.

The chorus has this complaint:

Our Jimmy, farewell! Your brothers fell
Way down in Alabarmy.
I thought they would spare
A lone widder's heir,
But they grafted him into the army.

228. "CHEER UP COMRADES, THEY WILL COME"

Tramp! Tramp! Tramp! The Prisoners Hope. Words & music by Geo. F. Root. Chicago, 1865. MUS

The prisoner-of-war, Union and Confederate alike, could only hope that he would survive the horrors of his existence until he could be rescued by the armed forces of his nation. On this theme, George F. Root produced one of the great marching songs. "Tramp! Tramp! Tramp!" or "The Prisoner's Hope" was published in 1863 and remained popular throughout the war. The song crossed the lines and a Confederate version, only slightly altered in its lyrics, had some popularity. The success of the song led the ambitious and prolific Root to a sequel, "On! On! On! The Boys Came Marching," or "The Prisoner Free." A comic parody, "The Bounty Jumper's Lament," contained the line "Tramp! Tramp! Tramp! The guard came marching."

229. THE HOMECOMING SONG OF AMERICAN SOLDIERS

When Johnny Comes Marching Home. Words and music by Louis Lambert [pseud.]. Boston, 1863. MUS

This song, more commonly associated with the Spanish-American War, is one of the great contributions of the Civil War to American music. Its composer was an Irish-born musician who became one of America's most famous bandmasters, Patrick Sarsfield Gilmore, who employed the pen-name of "Louis Lambert" for his best-known work. The origin of the lilting melody is somewhat controversial; some authorities trace it to an old Irish folk-song, "Johnny, I Hardly Knew Ye," but Gilmore's association is otherwise undisputed. Although the song quickly became an expression of both soldiers and civilians for a return of peace, it is more likely that Gilmore intended it to celebrate the return of discharged or furloughed soldiers. Copyrighted in Boston on September 26, 1863, the joyous homecoming song, widely used in every American war since, is possibly associated with the 24th Massachusetts Volunteers, a regiment in which Gilmore and his famed band served until August 30, 1862. The copy of the song displayed states that the music was "introduced in The Soldier's Return March," also composed by Gilmore and dedicated to Capt. William V. Hutchings of the 24th Massachusetts, whose discharge in mid-April 1863 might have provided inspiration. The song was especially popular during 1864, when the 3-year enlistments of many regiments expired, and the veterans returned home on furlough before reenlisting. From the 24th Massachusetts, for example, 450 men reached Boston on reenlistment furloughs on February 20, 1864, and were welcomed by ceremonies which included music by Gilmore's band.

230. ANOTHER WAR FAVORITE

When This Cruel War is Over. Words by Charles C. Sawyer. Music by Henry Tucker. Macon and Savannah, [186–]. MUS

So destructive to morale were the sentiments expressed in "Weeping Sad and Lonely" or "When This Cruel War is Over" that some officers banned it in their commands. Despite such restrictions, this composition of Charles Carroll Sawyer and Henry Tucker gained an immense acceptance with sales of nearly a million copies. It was published first in New York. With a few slight but appropriate alterations in the lyrics (*e.g.,* "grey" for "blue"), the song became also a great favorite in the Confederacy. This Southern version was published by John C. Schreiner & Son, publisher also of music described in entries 223 and 224.

231. SOME LYRICS BY A FAMED AMERICAN POET

Jonathan to John. Words by Hosea Bigelow. Music composed by F. Boott. Boston, 1862. MUS

The *Trent* Affair and the possibility of British intervention in the early years of the war produced at least two songs. During the removal of the Confederate commissioners from the English vessel, the daughter of John Slidell slapped a Union lieutenant. The incident was memorialized in "The Gallant Girl that Smote the Dastard Tory, Oh!" (a composition of "Klubs" and "Ducie Diamonds"). In the fall of 1862 the Northern view of American-British relations was expressed in "Jonathan to John." Employing his famous pseudonym of "Hosea Biglow," James Russell Lowell wrote:

It don't seem hardly fair, John,
When both my hands was full,
To stump me to a fight, John,
Your cousin, tu, John Bull!

Old Uncle S. sez he, "I guess
We know it now," sez he,
"The Lion's paw is all the law,
Accordin' to J. B.
Thet's fit for you an' me!"

232. LEAVE-TAKING SONGS OF THE WAR

The Conscript Mother's Song. Words and music by Henry Bedlow. Arranged for the piano by P. Pfeiffer. Newport, R.I., 1863. Cover lithographed by Sarony, Major & Knapp, New York.   MUS

This song is one of several on the theme of the parting of mothers and sons. In it, as in other songs such as "His Country Needs Him More Than I," "She Stood at the Door," and "The Volunteer's Mother," patriotism overcomes maternal fears:

Away with all sighing! Away with all tears!
My boy shall behold, not my grief, but my pride,
Shall I taint his young manhood with womanish
    fears,
When the flag of his country is scorned and
    defied?

233. A SENTIMENTAL FAVORITE, NORTH AND SOUTH

The Vacant Chair; or, We Shall Meet, but We Shall Miss Him. Words by H. S. W. Music by G. F. Root. Richmond, [186–].   MUS

The death of Lt. John William Grout of Worcester, Mass., at Ball's Bluff in October 1861, was commemorated in verses composed by Henry S. Washburn. Grout, only 18 years old, had expected to be home on furlough for Thanksgiving. At the family dinner that day, his chair was left unoccupied; and Washburn, a guest, was moved to write a poem which first appeared in the Worcester *Spy*. Set to music in 1862 by George F. Root, "The Vacant Chair" was widely sung in both the North and South. One of the most sentimental musical compositions of the war, it has proved also one of the most enduring.

234. WAR SONG BY STEPHEN COLLINS FOSTER

"Willie, We Have Missed You. By the highly popular author Stephen C. Foster." New York, [186–]. Broadside.   MUS

Stephen Collins Foster, a Pennsylvanian whose beloved songs are indelibly identified with the South, moved to New York in 1860. Here he wrote prolifically, but with little success. The first of his war songs, "I'll Be a Soldier," was copyrighted in July 1861. The last, "Give This to Mother," was submitted to the publisher on January 10, 1864, just 3 days before his death. Among other songs of the war composed by Foster were: "We've a Million in the Field," "For the Dear Old Flag I Die," "Willie Has Gone to the War," and "Willie, We Have Missed You." These song sheets were often issued simultaneously with the sheet music. Known sometimes as "penny ballads," when printed without the music, these broadsides were widely distributed. Illustrations raised the price to 5 cents. The publisher of this sheet advised the reader: "Ten Illustrated songs on notepaper mailed to any address on receipt of 50 cts."

235. A ROUTINE SONG, LONG SINCE FORGOTTEN

I'm Looking For Him Home. A Beautiful Ballad Written and Composed by Will. S. Hays. Louisville, Ky., [1862].   MUS

A contemporary observer estimated that at least 2,000 musical compositions appeared during the first year of the war. The total output of the war may be five times that number. The overwhelming majority of these songs had little, if any, popularity and were quickly forgotten. Shown is an example of this flood of musical ephemera. The sentiment of the song was expressed in many other compositions, including one with a more earthy title, "Oh, Send My Old Man Home Again."

LOOKING TOWARD PEACE

At Gettysburg and at his second inauguration, Abraham Lincoln, in two brief addresses unique in their eloquence and insight, defined the purpose of the war and looked beyond it to a nation reunited. While others, powerful in their opposition, demanded vengeance and the complete subjugation of the South, he worked to establish a policy toward both individuals and States which would make the restoration of the Union as quick and as free from bitterness and vindictiveness as possible.

The imperishable documents displayed, in the handwriting of President Lincoln, were given by him to his secretary, John Hay, whose children (Helen Hay Whitney, Alice Hay Wadsworth, and Clarence L. Hay) presented them to the Library of Congress on April 11, 1916.

236. "FIRST DRAFT" OF THE GETTYSBURG ADDRESS

Two-page holograph document by Abraham Lincoln.   MSS

On November 2, 1863, Abraham Lincoln was invited to deliver a "few appropriate remarks" at the ceremonies, on November 19, setting aside a portion of the battlefield at Gettysburg as a national cemetery. This is the manuscript, in Lincoln's hand, which has become known as the "first draft" and which is generally accepted—regardless of when and where it was written—as the address as it was first written by Lincoln. It

is almost certain that this draft, in part at least, was written in Washington prior to the departure for Gettysburg. The first page is written in ink on Executive Mansion stationery and may represent what Lincoln meant when he told James Speed on November 17 (according to Speed's recollection in 1870) that he had found time to "write about half" of the address. The second page, in pencil on plain ruled paper, and a penciled addition at the foot of the first page strongly suggest that Lincoln worked on this draft on at least two different occasions. One of his secretaries, John G. Nicolay, reported 30 years later that Lincoln carried in his pocket that part of the address he had written in Washington, *i.e.* the first page of the first draft, and that at the home of David Wills in Gettysburg he completed it in pencil on the morning of November 19. Some scholars believe that the second page was written in Gettysburg on the evening of November 18. Other authorities have noted that the first page ends in an incomplete sentence and have suggested that the second page is not necessarily Lincoln's first writing of it.

237. "SECOND DRAFT" OF THE GETTYSBURG ADDRESS

Two-page holograph document by Abraham Lincoln.   MSS

This draft of the address is written in ink on two sheets of paper identical with that used for the second page of the "first draft." In this version Lincoln added two sentences: "It is altogether fitting and proper that we should do this," and "It is for us, the living, rather to be dedicated here to the unfinished work which they have, thus far, so nobly carried on." The words in the first draft, "for those who died here, that the nation might live," have been changed to read: "for those who here gave their lives that that nation might live." In addition, it is generally agreed that Lincoln did not speak verbatim from the manuscript; and that possibly some of the corrections on this draft were made after he had finished speaking, to make the manuscript conform to what he had said.

It is not definitely known when and where Lincoln wrote this draft. Some scholars believe Lincoln wrote it in Gettysburg on the morning of the ceremony and that it is the manuscript which he held in his hand while he spoke. Others believe that it was written out later at the request of his secretary, John Hay. These beliefs may or may not be correct. In all Lincoln wrote at least five versions of the address. In addition to the two drafts, he prepared three other copies, at various times after November 19, for sale for charitable purposes at Sanitary fairs.

238. THE AUTHOR OF THE GETTYSBURG ADDRESS

Photograph by Alexander Gardner, Nov. 1863. **P**

This full-face portrait of the President, one of the best-known and most widely circulated of his photographs, was one of a series made in Washington by Gardner a few days prior to the delivery of the Gettysburg Address.

239. TOWARD "A JUST AND LASTING PEACE"

Second Inaugural Address. Two-page holograph document by Abraham Lincoln, with printed copy of the address. **MSS**

In the address delivered at his second inauguration, March 4, 1865, Abraham Lincoln expressed his hope for peace and a restoration of the Union. The nobility of his sentiments of generosity and good will have made this brief address one of his most enduring. The London *Times* described it as "the most sublime State paper of the century." Of it Lincoln himself wrote: "I expect [it] to wear as well as—perhaps better than—anything I have produced; but I believe it is not immediately popular. Men are not flattered by being shown that there has been a difference of purpose between the Almighty and them. To deny it, however, in this case, is to deny that there is a God governing the world . . . ."

The address closes with words known and loved by millions throughout the world:

With malice toward none; with charity for all; with firmness in the right, as God gives us to see the right, let us strive on to finish the work we are in; to bind up the nation's wounds; to care for him who shall have borne the battle, and for his widow and his orphan—to do all which may achieve and cherish a just and a lasting peace, among ourselves and with all Nations.

List of Negatives

INFORMATION ON ORDERING PHOTOGRAPHS

In the absence of copyright restrictions or other conditions, photocopies may be secured of all exhibited materials belonging to the Library of Congress. Orders should be addressed to the Photoduplication Service, Library of Congress, Washington 25, D.C. A request should be accompanied by a full description of the item and its location as indicated by a symbol after the entry in this catalog. Where photographic negatives already exist, the negative number should also be indicated as shown below.

Photographs in the Brady-Handy Collection (see entry nos. 145, 151, and 159) cannot be reproduced without the permission of Mrs. Alice H. Cox, daughter of the late Levin C. Handy, Washington photographer; there will be no restriction on use of the collection after September 14, 1964.

Entry No.	Photographic Negative No.	Entry No.	Photographic Negative No.
3	LC–USZ62–9648	43	LC–USZ62–38
4	LC–USZ62–10704	44	LC–B8171–7879
5	LC–USZ62–11191	45	LC–B8171–7165
8	LC–USZ62–15626	47	LC–USZ62–14262
14–2	LC–USZ62–15716	49	LC–USZ62–140
15	LC–USZ62–4521	51	LC–USZ62–15605
16	LC–USZ62–15706	53	LC–B8171–2358
17–1	LC–B8184–10374	54	LC–USZ62–3579
17–2	LC–B8184–10088	55	LC–USZ62–1144
17–3	LC–B8184–10018	58	LC–B8171–7951
17–4	LC–B8184–10338	59	LC–USZ62–15625
17–5	LC–B8184–10037	61	LC–USZ62–15696
17–6	LC–B8184–10086	63–1	LC–USZ62–145
18	LC–USZ62–35	63–2	LC–USZ62–1262
20	LC–B8184–10016	64	LC–USZ62–15698
21	LC–USZ62–15703	65	LC–USZ62–15621
22	LC–USZ62–12795	66	LC–USZ62–13184
23	LC–USZ62–37	67	LC–USZ62–15711
24	LC–USZ62–15697	68	LC–USZ62–1264
25	LC–USZ62–1143	69	LC–USZ62–4369
28	LC–B8184–10006	71	LC–B8171–730
29	LC–B8184–10051	72	LC–USZ62–7056
32	LC–B8184–4546	73	LC–USZ62–7060
36	LC–USZ62–1794	74	LC–USZ62–15336
38	LC–USZ62–138	77	LC–B8171–951
39	LC–USZ62–14837	78	LC–USZ62–14768
40	LC–USZ62–15708	79	LC–USZ62–2480
41	LC–USZ62–667	80	LC–B8184–7193
42	LC–USZ62–1071	84	LC–USZ62–14709

We call the reader's attention also to the Library's recent publication Civil War Photographs, 1861–1865: A Catalog of Copy Negatives Made from Originals Selected from the Mathew B. Brady Collection in the Prints and Photographs Division of the Library of Congress. *It may be purchased from the Photo-duplication Service, Library of Congress, Washington 25, D.C., at 75 cents a copy. Prints from the negatives listed in the catalog may also be purchased from the Photoduplication Service, as well as a 35mm. positive film (at $15 a copy, postpaid), which contains all the photographs described in the catalog.*

Index

The following index to the catalog includes not only subjects and the names of persons and places, but (in italics) the names of ships and the titles of books, pamphlets, and periodicals, and (in Roman within quotation marks) the titles of music, prints, drawings, and broadsides. The numbers indicate entries, except occasional numbers in italics which refer to pages. Where both types of numbers occur in the same line, the numbers for pages are to be found after those for entries, from which they usually are separated by a semicolon. Under "Brady, Mathew B.," for example, the series of numbers preceding the semicolon refer to entries, and the italicized numbers following the semicolon refer to pages.

88

U.S. GOVERNMENT PRINTING OFFICE: 1951